Key Stage 3
Developing Literacy

TEXT LEVEL

READING AND WRITING ACTIVITIES
FOR LITERACY LESSONS

Christine Moorcroft and Ray Barker

A & C BLACK

Contents

Acknowledgements

The authors and publishers are grateful for permission to reproduce the following:

p. 10 extract from *Letts Study Guide: KS3 History* by Peter Lane and Christopher Lane (Letts, 1995); extract from *Collins Encyclopedia of Scotland* edited by John Keay and Julia Keay; extract from *Scotland: The Story of a Nation* by Magnus Magnusson (HarperCollins, 2000); **p. 18** extract from *One Hundred Ways for a Cat to Train its Human* by Celia Haddon (Hodder & Stoughton, 2001). Reproduced by permission of Hodder and Stoughton Limited; **p. 20** text adapted from *In School, Stay Cool: A YoungMinds Booklet.* Reproduced by permission of YoungMinds, www.youngminds.org.uk; **p. 22** extract from 'The Second World War' by Elizabeth Jennings (from *Welcome to the Party*, BBC Books, 1993); extract from 'Soldiers' by Terry Jones (from *Welcome to the Party*, BBC Books, 1993); **p. 26** extract from *The Wind in the Willows* by Kenneth Grahame (Penguin, 1908); extract from *The Stone Book Quartet* by Alan Garner (Collins, 1983). Reproduced by permission of HarperCollins Publishers Ltd © Alan Garner, 1983; **p. 30** extract from *The Other Side of Truth* by Beverley Naidoo (Puffin, 2000). Copyright © Beverley Naidoo, 2000; **p. 34** extract from *Cider with Rosie* by Laurie Lee published by Hogarth Press. Used by permission of The Random House Group Limited; **p. 38** extract from *Revolting Rhymes* by Roald Dahl (Jonathan Cape Ltd, 1982); **p. 42** text adapted from *Looking at Materials* by Peter Stokes (Thomas Nelson and Sons, 1976); **p. 48** text adapted from 'The Sporting Spirit' from *Shooting an Elephant and other essays* by George Orwell (Copyright © George Orwell, 1936) by permission of Bill Hamilton as the Literary Executor of the Estate of the Late Sonia Brownell Orwell and Secker & Warburg Ltd; **p. 62** extract from *Watership Down* by Richard Adams (Penguin, 1973).

Published 2004 by A & C Black Publishers Limited
37 Soho Square, London W1D 3QZ
www.acblack.com

ISBN 0-7136-6487-8

Copyright text © Christine Moorcroft and Ray Barker, 2004
Copyright illustrations © Jean de Lemos, 2004
Copyright cover illustration © Paul Cemmick, 2004
Editor: Lucy Poddington

The authors and publishers would like to thank Claire Truman for her advice in producing this series of books.

A CIP catalogue record for this book is available from the British Library.

Printed in Great Britain by St Edmundsbury Press Ltd, Bury St Edmunds, Suffolk.

A & C Black uses paper produced with elemental chlorine-free pulp, harvested from managed sustainable forests.

Key Stage 3 Developing Literacy: Text Level is a series of photocopiable resources for Years 7, 8 and 9, designed to be used during English lessons or in other subjects across the curriculum to improve reading, writing and speaking and listening skills. The activities are also ideal for homework. The books focus on the Text level strand of the Key Stage 3 National Strategy *Framework for teaching English: Years 7, 8 and 9.*

Each book supports the teaching of English by providing a series of activities that develop essential literacy skills. These include reading and the interpretation of texts (fiction and non-fiction), writing and the communication of ideas for specific purposes and in appropriate styles – as well as speaking and listening. All of these are about communication, and demand that the reader, writer or speaker is in control of his or her material and uses language appropriately.

Text Level Year 8 develops the pupils' appreciation and awareness of each of these aspects. In particular, it helps them to understand the need to tailor a text to match the needs of specific audiences and purposes. The pupils are encouraged to develop skills in a way which is progressive as well as transferable to different contexts. These skills include:

- undertaking independent research using a range of reading strategies;
- investigating how writers convey meaning and develop ideas;
- interpreting literary texts and recognising how they reflect their time, culture or setting;
- experimenting with language to convey character and setting and to establish tone;
- explaining complex information clearly, orally and in writing;
- presenting a balanced analysis of an issue;
- interacting effectively in group discussion.

How to use this book

Each double-page spread in this book is based on a Year 8 Text level objective. The left-hand page is a **starter** activity, which may be an OHT for use with the whole class, or an activity for the pupils to work on in pairs or small groups. The right-hand page provides a **consolidation** activity to reinforce the main teaching objective, followed by an **extension** activity (**Now try this!**) to extend the pupils' learning.

Starter activities

Each starter activity is designed to be used as a short introduction to the consolidation activity that follows it. Evidence has shown that lessons which start with a sharp focus on a specific objective – for only ten to fifteen minutes – grab the pupils' attention and ensure that the whole class is clear about what to do and about the expected outcome of the lesson. The starter activities in this book address the objectives in a direct and explicit way. They involve both reading and writing, and encourage fast-paced learning and interaction. Various teaching and learning styles are used – from independent to teacher supported – focusing on the following key teacher interactions:

- direction
- modelling
- explanation
- exploration
- discussion
- demonstration
- scaffolding
- questioning
- investigation
- reflection and evaluation.

The starter activities in this book also provide valuable opportunities to revise previous learning. New terms are introduced and other important terms are revised during the starter activity; these are highlighted by being boxed or set in bold type. All the highlighted terms are explained in the glossary on page 64, which can be photocopied for the pupils to file and use for reference.

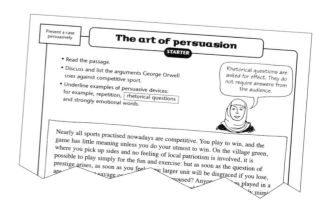

The starter activities can be photocopied and used in the following ways:

- as an OHT for whole-class teaching, with pupils giving answers orally or coming to the front to help complete the sheet;
- as a group activity, with each group working through the sheet or with different groups focusing on different parts of the sheet;
- as a timed activity, with the pupils completing as much of the sheet as possible within a time limit;
- in conjunction with appropriate class texts to help illustrate a principle;
- as preparatory work for an investigation, to be carried out for homework;
- as a stand-alone revision sheet for groups or individuals;
- as a tool for assessment.

Consolidation activities

The *Framework for teaching English: Years 7, 8 and 9* advocates that lessons should continue with a development of the main teaching points. The consolidation activities in this book can be used as the focus of this development, freeing teachers to work intensively with groups or individuals on the current objective.

The instructions in the activities are presented clearly to enable pupils to work independently. There are also opportunities for the pupils to work in pairs or groups, to encourage discussion and co-operation. Hints and reminders are given in boxes at the page margin.

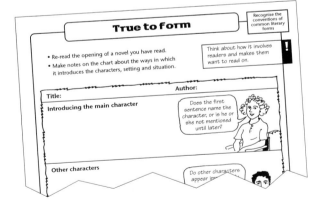

Extension activities

Each page ends with a **Now try this!** extension activity. These more challenging activities may be appropriate for only some of the pupils; it is not expected that the whole class should complete them. The pupils may need to record their answers in a notebook or on a separate piece of paper.

Organisation

The activities require very few resources besides dictionaries and thesauruses. Occasionally it may be useful to have available examples of texts such as: fictional and non-fictional recounts, reports (from booklets, leaflets and reference books), discussions and arguments (from newspapers, magazines or the Internet), and persuasive texts such as advertisements and charity or political leaflets. For some of the activities the pupils will need access to the Internet and resources in the school library.

All the activities in this book are linked closely to the requirements of the *Framework for teaching English*, but it is not intended that they should be presented in any specific order, unless stated. This resource is versatile and is intended for teachers to use according to the literacy needs of their pupils.

Some of the activities can be linked with work in other subjects; however, it is envisaged that most of the activities will be carried out during English lessons.

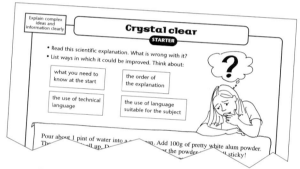

Teachers' notes

The notes provided at the foot of the activity pages contain additional instructions for using the sheets. These can be masked before photocopying. The notes on pages 6–9 offer further practical advice on making the most of the activity sheets, including extra lesson ideas and suggestions for introducing the teaching objectives.

Useful websites

Websites which you may find useful include: www.gutenberg.net, www.bartleby.com and www.penguinclassics.com (for access to a range of free texts), www.shakespeares-globe.org and www.shakespeare.com (for Shakespeare resources), www.englishresources.co.uk (for English resources, including units of work), www.literatureproject.com (a collection of classic books, poems, speeches and plays) and http://vtc.ngfl.gov.uk/docserver.php (Virtual Teacher Centre – a wealth of resources and information on literacy and other subjects).

Teachers' notes

The notes below expand upon those provided at the foot of each activity page. They give ideas for making the most of the activity sheets, including suggestions for follow-up work based on the sheet and answers to selected activities.

Reading

Pull it together (pages 10–11). This activity develops the pupils' ability to read non-fiction purposefully, to find specific information. In the **starter** activity they need to deduce information from the text, beginning with the relationships between Mary Queen of Scots and Henry VII and between Elizabeth I and Henry VII. Mary Queen of Scots was a great-granddaughter of Henry VII and Elizabeth was his granddaughter. However, Elizabeth's legitimacy was challenged by Roman Catholics. The chart in the **consolidation** activity should be used to answer another question which does not have a straightforward answer, such as whether a particular monarch was a popular ruler. The **extension** activity (**Now try this!**) encourages the pupils to investigate, and analyse the reasons for, any conflicting evidence they have found on the topic.

Quiz time (pages 12–13). This activity gives the pupils practice in using books, CD-ROMs and the Internet for research. The **starter** activity involves finding information as quickly as possible in a way which is competitive and fun. The pupils are required to use their skills in selecting an appropriate source and in using that source efficiently. This involves scanning the contents page and index of a book or the opening page and hyperlinks of a website and deciding which part of the resource will be the most useful. They could use a search engine such as Google. The answers are: (1) National Aeronautics and Space Administration, (2) basset hound, (3) red, white and black, (4) Liverpool and Sunderland, (5) platypus and echidna, (6) Lord Leverhulme, (7) resin from coniferous trees, (8) Antony Gormley, (9) 78 ft (23.77 m). The **consolidation** activity provides a structure which can be used for carrying out research in other subjects.

Short cuts (pages 14–15). This activity encourages the pupils to investigate different ways of making notes. In the **starter** activity, different methods may prove useful for the different passages: the first one is structured chronologically and so a timeline would be a helpful framework; the second is chronological with choices, and so choice-boxes linked by arrows might be a good idea; the third is technical and structured chronologically, and so a diagram using lines, boxes and arrows is suitable; the fourth could be recorded in note form using abbreviations for common words. The **consolidation** activity provides a linear flow chart for recording an explanation briefly; this is also suitable for planning other texts which need to be written in a chronological order, such as recounts and instructions. The pupils will need to read an explanation of a process; this could be linked with science (for example, how to separate materials), PSHE (for example, what happens when someone is arrested), geography (for example, how stalactites and stalagmites are formed) or history (for example, why a particular war was fought). The **extension** activity encourages the pupils to consider what is lost when a passage is rewritten in a shorter way.

Is that a fact? (pages 16–17). The focus of this activity is the way in which facts differ from opinions, ideas or theories. The **starter** activity helps the pupils to appreciate that facts can be checked in more than one source. Sometimes opinions are expressed as if they were facts: for example, *That is the best song she ever recorded*; *Apples are good for you*. It may be useful to discuss these examples and to compare them with facts which can be checked: for example, *In a poll, 90% of people said it was the best song she ever recorded*; *Apples contain vitamin C, which helps to protect the skin from scurvy*. The **consolidation** and **extension** activities help the pupils to distinguish between facts and opinions in their own writing and lead them to understand how facts can support or oppose opinions.

Be ironic! (pages 18–19). This encourages the pupils to recognise how humour is used in ironic writing. In the passage in the **starter** activity, irony arises from the situation, which is a reversal of the norm. The language and tone are ironic in that they mimic those of pet training manuals. The **consolidation** activity invites the pupils to create irony in their own writing in a similar way. As a follow-up, this type of role-reversal could be used as the basis for ironic writing on other themes: for example, a car writing a 'human-maintenance' manual or a computer writing about how to handle difficulties with its owner.

Order, order! (pages 20–21). This activity focuses on the order in which texts are structured: this could be chronological (for example, recounts, autobiographies or instructions) or logical (for example, arguments or explanations). The text in the **starter** activity needs to have certain parts in particular places (the introduction and any resources or reference material), but other parts could be in any order. The correct order of the pages of this leaflet is: *In School, Stay Cool: A YoungMinds Booklet, About this booklet, Coping with work?, Doing what your friends want and doing what you want, Bullying, What if I don't want to go to school?* and *Help section*. The first two pages (the title and introduction) can be in no other order and the last one (references for help) is best placed at the end, but the other sections could be in any order. The **consolidation** activity provides formats to help the pupils summarise texts which must be written in chronological order. The **extension** activity asks them to develop their own format for a non-chronological text.

Theme thoughts (pages 22–23).

This activity helps to show the different ways in which a theme can be presented. The poems in the **starter** activity are all about war, but the theme is treated differently in each piece of writing: 'The Second World War' conveys the fear of children whose only knowledge of war is from history lessons and toys and games; 'Soldiers' has a satirical tone, presenting war as a game played by powerful people; and 'The Charge of the Light Brigade' focuses on the bravery of the troops who followed the order to advance into a situation which gave little chance of survival. You could also provide contemporary news articles about war and ask the pupils to comment on the point of view of the writer and the tone of the writing. In the **consolidation** activity, the pupils apply what they have learned to texts on a different theme, investigating how the mood and tone are established. This could be linked with other texts the pupils are studying.

Deeper and deeper (pages 24–25).

This activity looks at ways of interpreting texts. The **starter** activity presents the reading log of someone who reads Philip Pullman's *Northern Lights*, viewing it at first as an exciting story with plenty of mystery and action and then beginning to understand its deeper meanings and what the writer is saying. This log can be used to show the pupils that they are not expected to gain a complete understanding of a difficult book, but to notice the way in which their understanding can deepen through careful reading. The **consolidation** activity invites the pupils to use this as a model for their own reading of a complex book. They could re-read a text they have studied at school or they could begin a new text, using this as part of their reading journal.

True to form (pages 26–27).

This activity draws out some of the conventions of novels for older children: the introduction of the main character near the beginning of the book (usually in the first sentence) and the setting of the scene and start of the action. In the **starter** activity, the first and second passages begin the action almost immediately, drawing the reader straight into the story, but in the third the reader is first acquainted with the setting. The **consolidation** and **extension** activities require the pupils to look at other novels for comparison. You could discuss similarities and differences between the structures of novels: for example, noticing the point at which they begin (at the beginning or in the middle of a story – or even at the end). The readers may be required to work out or imagine parts of the setting for themselves.

Past prose (pages 28–29).

This activity could be used in connection with the pupils' work in history; it encourages them to draw on their knowledge of the nineteenth century when reading a novel from that period. The **starter** activity presents two passages from *North and South* by Elizabeth Gaskell and a section from the back-cover blurb. Elizabeth Gaskell's writing reflected her passionate concerns about the hostility between working people and their employers, feeling that each group depended on the other. The pupils should notice the way in which the writer uses language to engage the readers' emotions: for example, in the contrast between the calm and confident language of Mrs Thornton and the impassioned speech of Nicholas Higgins' workmate. In the **consolidation** activity, the pupils investigate the ways in which other novelists of the time portrayed social conditions.

Put prose in its place (pages 30–31).

In this activity the pupils look at how literature reflects the values of the culture and place in which it is set. The passage in the **starter** activity is set in a country in which people risk their lives if they express criticism of the ruling regime. Sade's father is a journalist who has written a piece criticising his country's education system. Her mother has been shot and killed; the killing is clearly a punishment or warning. The **consolidation** activity provides a format on which the pupils record what they find out from the passage. You could ask them how they feel about the situation and what they think Mr Solaja should do – continue to write what he knows is the truth or 'toe the line' for safety. The pupils can look for language which communicates the tension in this situation. The lines in italics express Mr Solaja's beliefs, although today he is unusually silent and the words remain unspoken. His stillness is made all the more noticeable through the contrast with his brother and with his own habitual energetic activity: for example, *It was usually their father whose arms, hands, even fingers, danced like furious gymnasts... But today their father's arms hung without life.*

Writing

Room for improvement (pages 32–33). This activity helps the pupils to appreciate the need to communicate meaning effectively. The **starter** activity looks at the order of paragraphs and considers the use of adjectives in creating meaning. This is ideal for group work and for pairing pupils of different abilities to learn from one another. The **consolidation** activity develops this by showing the need for writers to follow rules of grammar and punctuation. The pupils could keep a copy of the proofreading symbols in their exercise books or folders so that they can refer to them when needed.

Cool comparisons (pages 34–35). In this activity the pupils investigate the effects of figurative language. The passage in the **starter** activity uses figurative language to create a vivid picture of a frosty morning. The pupils should be aware that being able to identify similes and metaphors is not enough; they need to understand why the writer used the comparisons and be able to describe their effect. The **consolidation** activity looks at personification as a type of metaphor, and the **extension** activity provides a format to help the pupils plan and write a poem of their own using personification.

Tone up! (pages 36–37). The tone of a piece of writing communicates the way in which ideas are expressed. The **starter** activity uses speaking and listening to introduce the idea of tone, and the **consolidation** activity develops this into written work. The pupils should consider the effect they wish to create before they write each sentence (this links with the planning and drafting activity on pages 32–33). In the **extension** activity, the pupils develop one of their sentences into a paragraph. If they include dialogue, they could make use of the verbs in the starter activity.

Time for an update (pages 38–39). In this activity the pupils experiment with ways of retelling traditional stories. The **starter** activity uses a poem by Roald Dahl as an example. Roald Dahl subverts the stereotype of the innocent young girl and the nasty wolf (the 'goodie' and the 'baddie'). He uses language which makes the story suitable for an older audience. His aim is to create humour but also to bring a sense of realism into the story-telling. Fairy tales were originally very violent folk tales but were rewritten in the eighteenth century as moral tales for young children. In a sense, Roald Dahl takes the story back to its origins. The **consolidation** activity allows the pupils to write their own modern version of one of Aesop's fables, using a writing frame to plan their ideas.

All kinds of poems (pages 40–41). Here the pupils investigate different forms and styles of poems, including how the same theme can be treated in different ways. The **starter** activity revises a variety of poetic forms. The answers are: (1) couplet, (2) ballad, (3) haiku, (4) sonnet, (5) cinquain, (6) free verse. This leads on to the **consolidation** activity, where the theme of death is considered using two different forms: a comic epitaph and a more serious free-verse poem. This can be linked with the activity on tone on pages 36–37.

Guide the reader (pages 42–43). This activity looks at the use of organisational devices and structure to help guide the reader through difficult material. The **starter** activity gives an example from a textbook which uses a variety of typestyles and diagrams to aid clarity. The **consolidation** activity asks the pupils to select and organise information for an explanation. The correct order for the five relevant sections is: (1) *To make and then pass a law in England [...] Then, with the help of civil servants, it will prepare a law in draft form.* (2) *The government then creates a 'green paper' [...] When this has happened, a revised 'white paper' is published.* (3) *After this, a bill is presented to the House of Commons [...] These need to be voted upon by all MPs present.* (4) *At the current time, when the new bill has been passed [...] They can return it to the Commons to be debated once again.* (5) *Finally, when both Houses approve the bill, it becomes law.*

Crystal clear (pages 44–45). This activity helps the pupils to organise and explain complex information. The **starter** activity looks at the features of a scientific explanation. In this passage the order should be chronological and it is not; the personal tone creeps in where it is not appropriate; the diagrams are not in a useful place; and the language should be more technical and precise. Often an explanation of an experiment uses the passive (for example, *the powder was added*) in order to distance the writer from the material. The **consolidation** activity provides a framework to help the pupils write their own explanation.

Get formal! (pages 46–47). This activity encourages the pupils to recognise and use suitable levels of formality in their writing. It links with the activity on tone on pages 36–37. The **starter** activity asks the pupils to think about situations in which different levels of formality may be used, taking account of the speaker and audience. This is developed in the **consolidation** activity in the context of a school prospectus, which requires formal language and style. As a follow-up, the pupils could look at a genuine school prospectus and analyse its style and level of formality.

The art of persuasion (pages 48–49). This activity looks at some of the techniques of persuasion. The **starter** activity provides a passage by George Orwell which features devices such as repetition and the use of rhetorical questions. The **consolidation** activity gives the pupils the opportunity to respond to Orwell's views and provides words and phrases which they can use in their arguments. The **extension** activity involves rewriting the arguments for a different audience, paying attention to changes in the style and tone.

Take my advice (pages 50–51). This activity helps the pupils to identify and use the features of various kinds of advice. The **starter** activity provides examples of two kinds of advice: one which orders the reader to do something and one which offers suggestions. The **consolidation** activity asks the pupils to give advice about an issue relevant to themselves. The style of writing in this task should be similar to that of passage 2 in the starter activity. In the **extension** activity, the pupils write text for a poster to advise young people about National Insurance contributions and income tax. The style here will be closer to that of passage 1 in the starter.

Analyse this (pages 52–53). In this activity the pupils balance views and present an objective analysis of an issue. The **starter** activity suggests appropriate language to help them achieve this. The **consolidation** activity encourages the pupils to consider the issues surrounding waste and the environment, with a view to writing a balanced analysis. To structure the analysis, the pupils could present an argument and a counter-argument in each paragraph, or each point could be dealt with in a separate paragraph.

Speaking and listening

Telling tales (pages 54–55). The emphasis of this activity is on speaking and listening, and the pupils' stories should not be written down. The **starter** activity provides questions to consider and a simple story structure to follow. The **consolidation** activity is a fun approach to genre and story-telling. It will be helpful to revise the characteristics of the genres featured. The pupils should plan the structure of the story before they begin speaking. The wild-cards in the **extension** activity are introduced part-way through the story to change the mood, tone or pace. The pupils are also given the opportunity to experiment with mixing elements from different genres.

Speak formally (pages 56–57). This activity helps the pupils to focus on the differences between the ways in which people communicate. This links with the activity on formal writing on pages 46–47. The **starter** activity shows many of the features of informal speech: use of 'fillers' such as *er* and *um*; pauses (indicated by ellipses); contractions and colloquialisms such as *geddit* and *yep*; repetition of words and phrases such as *OK* and *stuff*; false starts and changes of mind about what is going to be said; 'tag' questions such as *doesn't it?*; slang words; simple vocabulary; vague language such as *sort of, stuff*; extra words such as *right, oh*; exclamations; and non-standard grammar. The pupils should notice how few of these features there are in the second passage. The **consolidation** activity asks the pupils to analyse their own informal speech and convert it to more formal speech. If cassette recorders are not available, the pupils could transcribe one another's speeches.

From pictures to words (pages 58–59). This links to previous work on explanations (see pages 42–45). Here the pupils are asked to give information orally. The **starter** activity involves describing how to do exercises. The listener could either perform or draw what he or she thinks has been explained. The **consolidation** activity looks at story structure from the point of view of a film director. The pupils may sequence the images in any order, as long as they can explain what is happening and why the particular sequence has been chosen.

It's the way you say it (pages 60–61). This activity focuses on the different ways in which messages are conveyed. In the **starter** activity, the pupils make statements or requests in role. Different tones will be used depending on whether they expect or hope the instruction to be obeyed, or if they fear it might not be obeyed. Much depends on the relative status of speaker and listener. The **consolidation** activity develops this by asking the pupils to analyse the differences in more depth.

Adopt a role (pages 62–63). This activity helps the pupils to understand the different roles which are useful in discussions. The **starter** activity presents a discussion from fiction in which each of the four characters takes on a different role. Fiver knows what has to be done and can explain why, but is not sure how it should be done. Hazel supports him and has a good grasp of the feelings of the other rabbits; he thinks clearly but is not quick to put ideas into practice. Bigwig is the one who urges action. Blackberry's role is to listen, understand what the others want to do and suggest a course of action. The **consolidation** activity gives the pupils an opportunity to discuss a problem among themselves, with each participant adopting a particular role. In the **extension** activity, they evaluate the way in which the discussion was conducted.

Pull it together
STARTER

- Look for information from these sources to answer the question in the speech bubble. Underline the parts of the text which will help.

Why did many people think Mary Queen of Scots, instead of Elizabeth, should have been queen of England?

A

Catherine of Aragón's parents, King Ferdinand and Queen Isabella of Spain, planned for her to marry Arthur, the son of Henry VII, king of England. Arthur was fourteen and Catherine was fifteen when they married in 1501. Six months later Arthur died and Henry VII arranged for his younger son, Henry (later Henry VIII), to marry Catherine. Henry VIII wanted a son and heir and, although Catherine gave birth to several babies (including some sons), the only one who survived was Mary (Mary Tudor), born in 1516.

Adapted from *Brainwaves: Tudor Times* by Christine Moorcroft

B

In 1503 Henry VIII's sister Margaret married James IV of Scotland, but in 1512 Scotland sided with France and went to war against England. James was killed at the battle of Flodden in 1513. James V (1513–42) confirmed the alliance with France by marrying Mary of Guise. In 1542 he led Scotland into war against England: he died two weeks after the defeat at Solway Moss. His daughter Mary now became Queen of Scots.

Henry VIII wanted to arrange a marriage between his five-year-old son, Edward, and Mary, the 'baby Queen'. He hoped that this would end the threat from the North. However, in 1547 he sent an army to try to force the Scots to accept his proposal. The Scots sent the five-year-old Mary to France, leaving her mother, Mary of Guise, to rule in her place. Ten years later, the Queen of Scots married the French king's eldest son and when he became king she became Queen of France.

From *Letts Study Guide: KS3 History* by Peter Lane and Christopher Lane

C

James V (1513–42) King – Elder and only surviving son of James IV and Margaret Tudor, James V succeeded his father when he was only 17 months old.

From *Collins Encyclopedia of Scotland* edited by John Keay and Julia Keay

D

In November of that year (1558) Queen Elizabeth ascended the throne of England. In Catholic eyes she was illegitimate – Henry VIII's divorce from Catherine of Aragón had never been recognised by the Catholic church, so his marriage to Elizabeth's mother, Anne Boleyn, had been void. Consequently, Mary Queen of Scots, as a great-granddaughter of Henry VII, was regarded as the rightful heir to the English throne.

From *Scotland: The Story of a Nation* by Magnus Magnusson

Developing Literacy
Text Level
Year 8
© A & C BLACK

Pull it together

- On the chart, write a question to which you would like to find the answer. It could be linked with work in any subject.
- Research the answer using a range of different sources. Record what you find out on the chart.

Remember to record the title and author of books you use, and relevant page numbers.

!

Question: _____

Source	Notes

The answer to my question is: _____

_____

_____

_____

_____

_____

NOW TRY THIS!

- Make a note of any conflicting information you found in different sources.
- Do more research to find out which is correct.
- Record what you think might be the reasons for these differences.

Teachers' note The pupils will need access to resources in the school library. Encourage them to write a question which asks *Why?* or *How?* rather than *What? Who?* or *When?* They could mark the relevant pages of books with slips of paper or sticky notes, and make notes of the key words. When using leaflets or web page printouts, they can mark the text as they did in the starter activity.

Quiz time
STARTER

- Find the answers to the questions as quickly as possible. Start a timer as you begin.

You don't have to answer the questions in order.

!

Question	Answer	✔ or ✗
1. For what does the acronym NASA stand?		
2. The name of which type of hound comes from a French word meaning 'low'?		
3. What are the colours of the stripes on the Egyptian flag?		
4. Which teams were presented with the wrong medals at the 1992 FA Cup Final?		
5. Name two kinds of mammal that lay eggs.		
6. Which British industrialist complained, 'Half the money I spend on advertising is wasted; the trouble is, I don't know which half'?		
7. From what fossilised material is amber formed?		
8. Who was the sculptor of the giant 'Angel of the North' at Gateshead, in Tyne and Wear?		
9. What is the length of a standard tennis court?		

Time: _____ minutes _____ seconds

Teachers' note Split the class into small groups and give each group a copy of this page. Each group also needs a timer and access to the Internet and resources in the school library. Ask the pupils first to consider the advantages and disadvantages of using books, CD-ROMs and the Internet to answer different types of questions. Challenge them to answer all the questions as quickly as possible, or to answer as many as they can within a time limit. They might need help in using a contents page, illustrations list, glossary and index efficiently. Go through the answers at the end.

Developing Literacy
Text Level
Year 8
© A & C BLACK

Quiz time

Undertake independent research

- On the chart, write questions to which you need to know the answers.
- Use books and the Internet to find the answers.

Using books
Scan the contents page, illustrations list, index and glossary.

Using websites
Scan the home page and links.

Make a note of the title, author and publisher of books. Write down the addresses of websites.

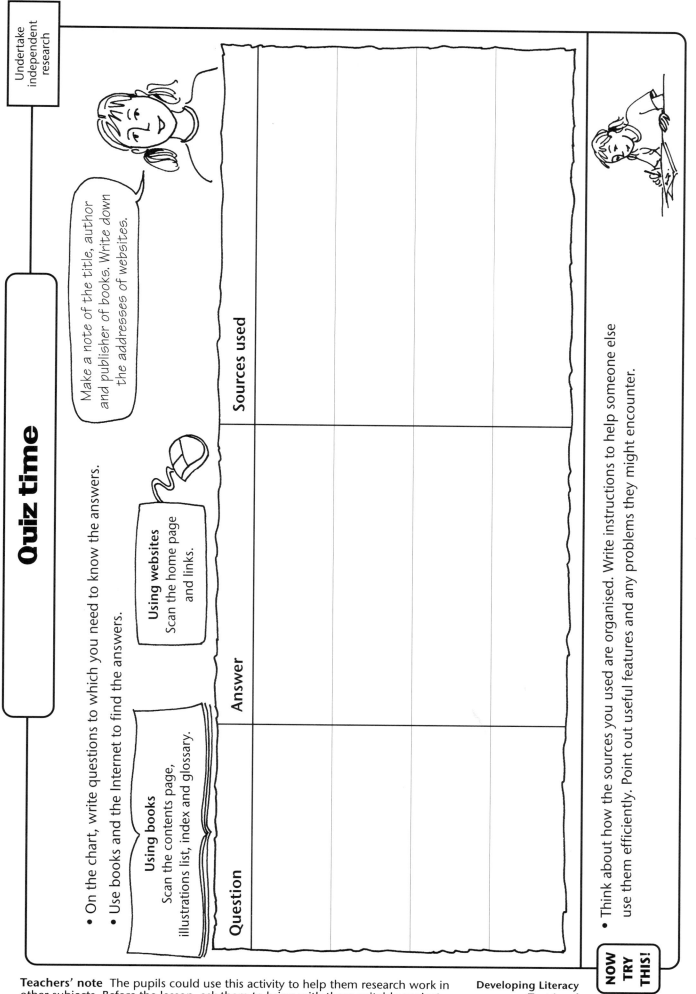

Question	Answer	Sources used

- Think about how the sources you used are organised. Write instructions to help someone else use them efficiently. Point out useful features and any problems they might encounter.

Teachers' note The pupils could use this activity to help them research work in other subjects. Before the lesson, ask them to bring with them suitable project work so that they can develop their research skills in a meaningful context. They will need access to the Internet and resources in the school library.

Developing Literacy
Text Level
Year 8
© A & C BLACK

Short cuts

STARTER

• Write the information in each box in the shortest possible way.

Use the most helpful method for each piece of text. You could use abbreviations, symbols, arrows and diagrams.

!

Longer version	Shorter version
1. Yesterday a woodcutter working in a forest near Nayland in Suffolk had the surprise of his life when he split a cedar log and revealed a quartz wristwatch embedded in the wood.	
2. To add a new email address, open Outlook Express, select File, then select Identities, then Add new identity. Where it says 'Enter your name', key in the name you want to use for the new identity. Tick the box if you want to add a password to protect your privacy. Click OK to get to the next frame. Decide whether you want to use the existing settings or change them, and follow the on-screen instructions.	
3. When you smell things, such as perfume, you actually breathe in some of the material. The material evaporates into the air and when it enters your nostrils some of its molecules eventually reach the smell receptors situated in the nasal cavity. The molecules can only be received by specific parts of the smell receptors, which send a message to your brain. Your brain then identifies the smell (for example, as 'oranges' or 'bad eggs').	
4. Villagers of Little Snoozeham have voiced strong objections to the proposed opening of a cattery in the residential area of Wailing Lane, saying that the noise would be unbearable. A spokesperson for the Little Snoozeham Residents Association says that she has recorded and analysed the noise made by only ten cats during one night and it exceeded permitted levels. "What is it going to be like with a hundred or more cats here?" she asked, adding that it would spoil a tranquil country village.	

Teachers' note Photocopy this page onto an OHT and cover all but the first item on the chart. Challenge the pupils to write (on paper) the information in the fewest possible words. Point out that they can write it in note form, as a diagram or as a flow chart, or in any other way they find helpful. Invite several pupils to write their versions on the board and compare different ways of communicating the same information. Count the number of characters each pupil has used and write the shortest version on the OHT. Repeat this for each item on the chart.

Developing Literacy
Text Level
Year 8
© A & C BLACK

Short cuts

- Read an explanation of a process.
- Make notes on the chart about the process.

You could draw labelled diagrams.

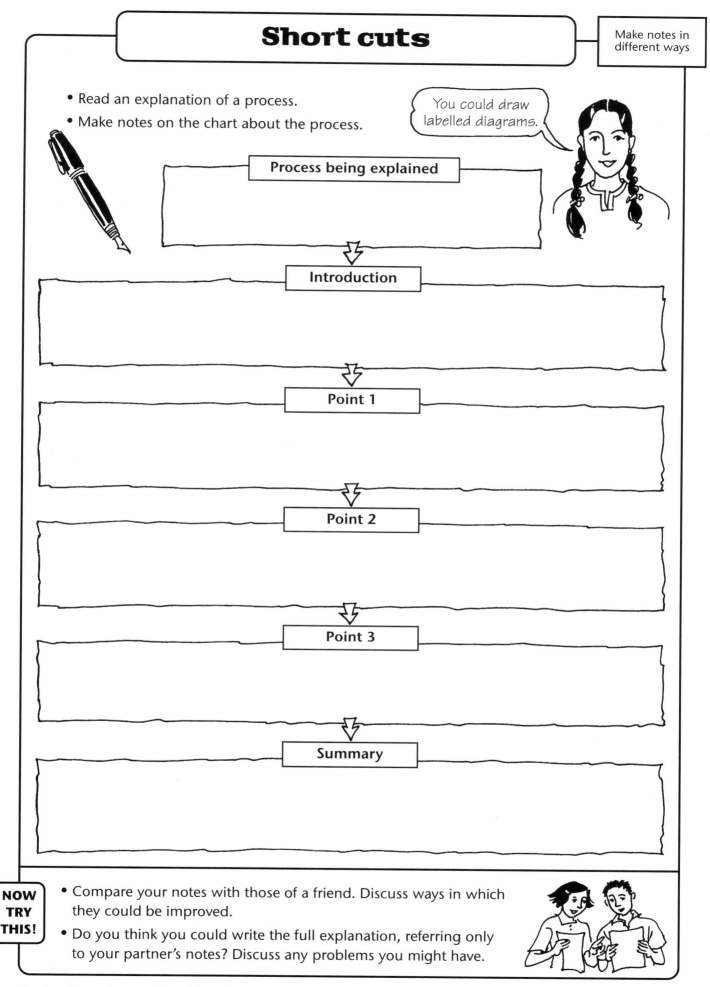

| Process being explained |

↓

| Introduction |

↓

| Point 1 |

↓

| Point 2 |

↓

| Point 3 |

↓

| Summary |

NOW TRY THIS!

- Compare your notes with those of a friend. Discuss ways in which they could be improved.
- Do you think you could write the full explanation, referring only to your partner's notes? Discuss any problems you might have.

Teachers' note The pupils could use this page to make notes for work in another subject, such as science or geography. Discuss why this format is suitable for recording the main points of an explanation. During the plenary session, point out that it may be useful to write some words and phrases in full (for example, names and technical words) in order to reinforce the correct spellings.

Developing Literacy
Text Level
Year 8
© A & C BLACK **15**

Is that a fact?

STARTER

• Read the speech bubbles. Which are | facts |? Which are opinions or theories?

1 A shortage of vitamin K causes the failure of the blood to clot.

2 The best way to cook fish is to steam it.

3 There might be a hidden path through the forest.

4 According to the travel book, there is a hidden path through the forest.

5 No one who has seen the Great Wall of China can fail to be impressed by its size.

6 The reporter said that no one who has seen the Great Wall of China can fail to be impressed by its size.

7 The best player in the match was Michael Owen.

8 Michael Owen scored three goals and was nominated 'Man of the Match' by the commentator.

9 It is going to be dry and cold tomorrow, with a sharp northeasterly wind.

10 Easter Island is uninhabited.

11 Easter Island was once covered with trees. Now there are none.

12 The lack of trees on Easter Island could have been caused by people who once lived there cutting them down to clear land for farming.

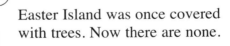

13 Easter Island is a forbidding-looking place, where no one would want to live.

Teachers' note Split the class into small groups and give each group a copy of this page. First revise the ways in which facts can be recognised (see page 6). Ask the pupils to make two lists, headed 'Facts' and 'Opinions or theories', and to write the number representing each statement in the correct list. After five minutes, ask for feedback and reinforce what makes a statement a fact (it can be checked and verified or corrected). Views such as *Apples are good for you* can be only supported by facts, rather than checked.

16

Developing Literacy
Text Level
Year 8
© A & C BLACK

Is that a fact?

- Choose a painting you have seen. Make notes on the charts to help you plan a magazine article about it. You will need to research and check **facts** about the painting. Use them to support your opinions, ideas and theories.

You could look at paintings at www.moma.com or www.tate.org.uk

Title of painting: _____   Artist: _____

Facts	Sources of facts

Opinions, ideas and theories	Evidence from the sources

NOW TRY THIS!

- Exchange notes with a partner.
- Check your partner's facts. If you disagree with them, say why.
- Read your partner's opinions, ideas and theories. If you disagree with them, say why.
- Make notes on how facts are different from opinions, ideas and theories.

Teachers' note The pupils will need access to the Internet or books of paintings. Encourage them to check all the facts they write. Revise that opinions, ideas and theories may be written as if they were facts, but the difference is that facts can be checked and proved to be true. During the plenary session, you could link this with work in science and discuss scientific theories.

Be ironic!

STARTER

- Read the passage. What do you notice about its tone ?
- Underline anything which makes you laugh.

The tone is the way the ideas are expressed.

!

Remember, humans have the mental age of a one-week-old blind kitten. They cannot express themselves in body language because they have no tail and no whiskers; their hair can't stand up and their ears are completely inflexible. They can learn only a few words from the huge body-language feline vocabulary.

Though humans cannot speak cat, they vocalise repeatedly. Most of their vocalisations are meaningless and can be safely ignored.

A few human vocalisations are worth remembering. Keep an ear open for one aversive human vocalisation – the 'vet' noise. When you hear this, leave home for the whole day or, if you are kept indoors, hide.

You may also detect a repeated sound such as 'Sam', 'Tibbles' or 'Sooty'. This sound marks a primitive human attempt at the kitten-call chirrup. Dogs come when they are called. We cats take a message and get back later – maybe.

A series of high-pitched human shrieks can mean either delight or fear. When these noises follow the gift of a mouse on the bed, we can safely guess that the reaction is one of delight at such a delicious present.

Ignoring your human by withdrawing your attention is a powerful training tool. Simply turn your back firmly away from the erring human, giving no eye contact, and sit quietly thinking of higher things.

To gain attention, place your bottom firmly on the newspaper your human is reading, being careful to cover the area scanned by its eyes.

Climb up a tree or a roof. Cling there, mewing. When your human tries to rescue you, climb higher. Eventually a large red engine and several beefy people in uniform will turn up. Wait until they start climbing up the ladder, then leap effortlessly down.

From *One Hundred Ways for a Cat to Train its Human* by Celia Haddon

---

Teachers' note Photocopy this page onto an OHT. Read the passage with the pupils and ask them by whom it is supposedly written. Point out that the tone is ironic; the passage presents a reversal of the expected situation (the usual kind of book on this topic would advise humans on training their pets). Invite the pupils to underline the things that make them laugh. You could show them a pet-training manual for comparison. Discuss that manuals of this sort often make assumptions about the mental capacities of animals; this passage applies the same kind of assumptions to humans.

Developing Literacy
Text Level
Year 8
© A & C BLACK

Be ironic!

- Use this page to plan a leaflet which is written as though the author is an animal in a zoo. The leaflet gives advice to new arrivals at the zoo on how to behave towards human visitors.

The **tone** of your writing should be **ironic**.

Introduction	
Rules	**Humorous explanations**
1. If a human approaches you carrying food, confiscate it immediately by any means necessary.	Luxury foods (e.g. ice creams) wasted on humans. Humans eat any old rubbish.
2.	
3.	
4.	
5.	
6.	
Summary	

NOW TRY THIS!

- Collect other examples of irony from books or electronic sources. Look for situations which do not match what is expected or which are presented in a mocking way.
- Explain what makes each example ironic.

Teachers' note Encourage the pupils to imagine they are animals in a zoo, watching the human visitors. Ask them to interpret and comment on things they might see and hear: for example, signs telling people not to feed or touch the animals, the comments made by people, and people's reactions to the behaviour of the animals.

Order, order!

STARTER

- Cut out these pages from a leaflet.
- Put them in an order which makes sense.

Where there are **ellipses** (…), text has been missed out to save space.

Coping with work?

You may feel you have a lot of juggling to do because of all the subjects you are taking at school. Some people find homework a big challenge. This might be because:

- you have to get used to working on your own and sometimes it is boring…
- you feel your homework takes too long…

Bullying

Bullying is an unhappy experience – certainly for the person being bullied but sometimes for the bully too. People can be bullied in different ways…

Doing what your friends want and doing what you want

Most people want to fit in with the crowd – have similar clothes, CDs and computer games, or go to the same places. Sometimes you might not have enough money, or you might want to do something different…

About this booklet

9 to 3, five days a week, school takes up a big part of your life…

This booklet describes some common problems and gives ideas on what to do about them. If you are worried about something which isn't included, you might find the help section at the end useful.

What if I don't want to go to school?

Everyone has days when they don't want to go to school. Sometimes people know the reasons, sometimes they don't. Possible reasons might be:

- you're having problems keeping on top of your work…
- you're not getting on with classmates…

In School, Stay Cool:

A YoungMinds Booklet

Help section

Here you will find useful contacts…

Teachers' note First point out that different types of text are structured in different ways to help readers find their way through them. Discuss that it is a good idea to 'skim' a non-fiction text to gain an overview of the subject matter and to find out whether it will be useful; and once this has been done, it is not necessary to read the whole text to find out the relevant information. After the pupils have arranged the pages in order, invite them to compare results and discuss why several different orders could be correct (see pages 6–7).

Developing Literacy
Text Level
Year 8
© A & C BLACK

Order, order!

- Choose two texts in which the ideas are organised in chronological order (following a time sequence).
- Write the title of each text. In the boxes, write a short summary of the main events.

You could choose recounts or explanations.

Text 1: _____   Text 2: _____

1.	1.
2.	2.
3.	3.
4.	4.
5.	5.

Continue on another sheet of paper if you need to.

NOW TRY THIS!

- Find an example of a non-chronological text, such as an argument or a non-chronological report.
- Draw a diagram to show how it is organised.

Write the main points in boxes. Link them in a way which shows how they are organised.

!

Teachers' note The pupils will need access to examples of chronological texts, such as instructions for using mobile phones or video recorders, or a recount of the events that happened during the reign of a monarch. For the extension activity, they will need examples of non-chronological texts, such as arguments or non-chronological reports.

Developing Literacy
Text Level
Year 8
© A & C BLACK   21

Theme thoughts
STARTER

- Read these passages.
- Discuss how the same theme is treated differently by each writer.

1

    The voice said 'We are at War'
And I was afraid, for I did not know what this meant.
My sister and I ran to our friends next door
As if they could help. History was lessons learnt
    With ancient dates, but here

    Was something utterly new,
The radio, called the wireless then, had said
That the country would have to be brave. There was much to do.
And I remember that night as I lay in bed
    I thought of soldiers who

    Had stood on our nursery floor
Holding guns, on guard and stiff. But war meant blood
Shed over battle-fields. Cavalry galloping. War
On that September Sunday made us feel frightened
    Of what our world waited for.

From 'The Second World War' by Elizabeth Jennings

2

If you're feeling jaded,
Or if you're feeling blue,
Have a little battle…
That's what the soldiers do.

When Genghis Khan was feeling bored
He'd gather up his Golden Horde
And say: 'Today we'll devastate
As far as Kiev.' And they'd say: 'Great!'

A Khan who wants to bring some charm
Into his life will spread some harm.
A little killing, here and there,
Gives life to armies everywhere.

From 'Soldiers' by Terry Jones

3

"Forward the Light Brigade!"
Was there a man dismay'd?
Not tho' the soldier knew
  Someone had blunder'd:
Theirs not to make reply,
Theirs not to reason why,
Theirs but to do and die:
Into the valley of Death
  Rode the six hundred.

From 'The Charge of the Light Brigade'
by Alfred Lord Tennyson

Teachers' note Photocopy this page onto an OHT. Read the poems with the class and identify the common theme. Ask the pupils what the writer of each text is saying; whether the tone is serious or humorous; whether the mood is romantic or practical and down-to-earth; whether the writer glorifies war or is against war; whether the text focuses on bravery or fear. Discuss how the language helps to convey the tone: for example, colloquial words such as *jaded* and *blue* contribute to the satirical tone of 'Soldiers'.

Developing Literacy
Text Level
Year 8
© A & C BLACK

Theme thoughts

- Collect and read some texts on a theme (such as animals, the environment, families, nature or the sea).
- Record on the chart the ways in which different writers treat the theme. Think about the writer's attitude to the theme, his or her opinions about it, and the purpose of the text.

The **mood** of the text might be calm, light-hearted or serious. The **tone** could be ironic, angry, regretful, persuasive, and so on.

Theme: _____

Text 1 title:		Author:	
Mood	Evidence	Tone	Evidence

Text 2 title:		Author:	
Mood	Evidence	Tone	Evidence

Text 3 title:		Author:	
Mood	Evidence	Tone	Evidence

NOW TRY THIS!

- Choose one of the texts. Comment on the way in which the writer uses language to communicate his or her views. Think about the choice of vocabulary and the use of dialogue, questions and exclamations.

Teachers' note Ask the pupils to work in groups of three and give each pupil a copy of this page. The group should choose a theme, then each of the three pupils should read and make notes on a different text. The texts could include poetry, fiction and non-fiction. The pupils can then come together to discuss and compare their ideas, and to collate their notes.

Revise and refine
interpretations
of a text

Deeper and deeper
STARTER

A reader has written down her thoughts as she reads a novel.

- How do her ideas about the book change as
  she reads it more and more carefully?

Title: *Northern Lights* **Author:** Philip Pullman

Beginning to read the book

The first chapter makes me want to read on. Why is this girl, Lyra, who is about eleven or twelve, living in a college at Oxford University? What is going on at the strange meeting of scholars which she overhears? I can't put it down. I have to finish it to find out what happens to Lyra and about the secret plans being made at the meeting. I think it is going to be a murder mystery story. The Master of the college seems to want to kill Lord Asriel, Lyra's uncle. I can't make out what age the book is set in. The places the scholars talk about have old-fashioned names, like Muscovy, and the technical equipment is not modern ('anbaric light' and 'naphtha lamps').

Reading on

There is a group of people called 'the Gobblers' who are kidnapping children. I can't really understand what they are doing to them; they seem to be torturing them to get something from them (this is the mysterious 'Dust' which Lyra hears being discussed at the college). The book seems to be set in a different world which exists alongside the one we know. I now think it is a kind of science fiction adventure. There are several plots. There is an evil woman called Mrs Coulter, who pretends to be kind (her slinky golden monkey gives her character away). She is one of the child-kidnappers – and now she has captured Lyra! The adventure is getting more exciting and scary. How is Lyra going to get away?

Beginning to understand

Lyra, and most other people in the book, has an animal which I thought was like a pet but it's a bit different – much closer than that. It is called a 'daemon' (pronounced 'demon'). People have different animals as daemons. Children's daemons can change from one animal to another, but adults' daemons are fixed. The animals seem to reflect their owners' personalities.

Thinking about it

The people who are kidnapping children seem to belong to a strange religious sect. They believe that if they can get this 'Dust' from enough children, they will have some kind of power. Now I think the daemons are people's souls.

A deeper understanding

The author seems to be saying that the evil organisation which is looking for 'Dust' is the Church. There is more than one mysterious world in the book. One of them might be heaven. There is something called 'the Authority'. This might be God. I am not sure what Lyra's role is, but she has a special and very important task which can affect everyone in the world.

Teachers' note For this activity the pupils need to have read, or be in the process of reading, a substantial text which requires careful reading in order to understand all its layers of meaning. Photocopy this page onto an OHT, cover the lower part of the chart and read the first paragraph with the pupils. If they have read *Northern Lights*, they could compare this reader's experience with their own understanding of the book when they began to read it. Uncover the chart a section at a time, reading it and discussing how the reader's understanding of the book changes.

Developing Literacy
Text Level
Year 8
© A & C BLACK

Deeper and deeper

- Record the way in which your understanding of a book changes as you read it. Write your thoughts on the chart.

Title: _____ **Author:** _____

Beginning to read the book

_____

_____

_____

Reading on

_____

_____

_____

_____

Beginning to understand

_____

_____

_____

Thinking about it

_____

_____

_____

A deeper understanding

_____

_____

_____

_____

NOW TRY THIS!

- Discuss what you have written with someone else who has read the same book. Compare what each of you thought about the book at different points.
- On the back of this sheet, write about any new ideas you have as a result of your discussion.

Teachers' note For this activity the pupils need to have read, or be in the process of reading, a substantial text which requires careful reading in order to understand all its layers of meaning. Encourage the pupils to use the chart in the starter activity as a model. Make sure, for the purposes of the extension activity, that some pupils choose the same books.

**Developing Literacy
Text Level
Year 8**
© A & C BLACK **25**

True to form
STARTER

• Read these openings of novels. Think about how they introduce the main characters and the situations.

1 Down the Rabbit-Hole

Alice was beginning to get very tired of sitting by her sister on the bank, and of having nothing to do: once or twice she had peeped into the book her sister was reading, but it had no pictures or conversations in it, 'and what is the use of a book,' thought Alice, 'without pictures or conversation?'

So she was considering in her own mind (as well as she could, for the hot day made her feel very sleepy and stupid), whether the pleasure of making a daisy-chain would be worth the trouble of getting up and picking the daisies, when suddenly a White Rabbit with pink eyes ran close by her.

There was nothing so *very* remarkable in that; nor did Alice think it so *very* much out of the way to hear the Rabbit say to itself, 'Oh dear! Oh dear! I shall be too late!' (when she thought it over afterwards, it occurred to her that she ought to have wondered at this, but at the time it all seemed quite natural); but when the Rabbit actually *took a watch out of its waistcoat-pocket*, and looked at it, and then hurried on, Alice started to her feet, for it flashed across her mind that she had never before seen a rabbit with either a waistcoat-pocket, or a watch to take out of it, and burning with curiosity, she ran across the field after it, and fortunately was just in time to see it pop down a large rabbit-hole under the hedge.

From *Alice's Adventures in Wonderland* by Lewis Carroll

2 The River Bank

The Mole had been working very hard all the morning, spring-cleaning his little home. First with brooms, then with dusters; then on ladders and steps and chairs, with a brush and a pail of whitewash; till he had dust in his throat and eyes, and splashes of whitewash all over his black fur, and an aching back and weary arms. Spring was moving in the air above and in the earth below and around him, penetrating even his dark and lowly little house with its spirit of divine discontent and longing. It was small wonder, then, that he suddenly flung down his brush on the floor, said 'Bother!' and 'O blow!' and also 'Hang spring-cleaning!' and bolted out of the house without even waiting to put on his coat. Something up above was calling him imperiously, and he made for the steep little tunnel which answered in his case to the gravelled carriage-drive owned by animals whose residences are nearer to the sun and air. So he scraped and scratched and scrabbled and scrooged, and then he scrooged again and scrabbled and scratched and scraped, working busily with his little paws and muttering to himself, 'Up we go! Up we go!' till at last, pop! his snout came out into the sunlight.

From *The Wind in the Willows* by Kenneth Grahame

3

A bottle of cold tea; bread and a half onion. That was Father's baggin. Mary emptied her apron of stones from the field and wrapped the baggin in a cloth.

The hottest part of the day was on. Mother lay in bed under the rafters and the thatch, where the sun could send only blue light. She had picked stones in the field until she was too tired and had to rest.

Old William was weaving in the end room. He had to weave enough cuts of silk for two markets, and his shuttle and loom rattled all the time, in the day and the night. He wasn't old, but he was called Old William because he was deaf and hadn't married. He was Father's brother.

He carried the cuts to market on his back. Stockport was further, but the road was flatter. Macclesfield was nearer, but Old William had to climb Glaze Hill behind the cottage to get to the road.

From *The Stone Book Quartet* by Alan Garner

Teachers' note Give each pupil a copy of this page. Ask the pupils to read the passages and then to work in pairs, making notes about how the writer of each novel introduces it. They should think about what they can tell from each opening paragraph about the type of novel it is, the main characters, the situation and the setting. Discuss their findings. Highlight the differences between passage 3 and the first two; the main character, Mary, is not introduced until the third sentence (after another character, Mary's father, has been mentioned).

Developing Literacy
Text Level
Year 8
© A & C BLACK

True to form

- Re-read the opening of a novel you have read.
- Make notes on the chart about the ways in which it introduces the characters, setting and situation.

Think about how it involves readers and makes them want to read on.

!

Title: **Author:**

Introducing the main character

Does the first sentence name the character, or is he or she not mentioned until later?

Other characters

Do other characters appear immediately or are they introduced later?

Setting the scene

Is the setting described in detail at the start or is it revealed bit by bit?

The events

Does the action begin at once or does the author concentrate on characters and setting?

NOW TRY THIS!

- Make a note of the tense in which the novel openings are written.
- Find novels written in different tenses. Write about the difference this makes.

Teachers' note Ask the pupils to notice at what point characters are introduced and the effect of the timings of these introductions. Ask how they would feel if they read a long descriptive passage before being introduced to the main character of a novel. For the extension activity, the pupils should refer to the novel openings in the starter activity as well as the one they have written about.

Past prose
STARTER

- Read these passages from *North and South* by Elizabeth Gaskell.

- How does the writer convey the feelings of the characters about social issues of the time?

The book was written in 1854. This is the back-cover blurb.

Transplanted from the 'civilised' South, Margaret Hale enters a grim new world in industrial Milton-Northern. Appalled by the smoke and noise of the mills, and shocked by the independence of the workers, she still finds no common ground with the blunt Northern manufacturers – especially not with her father's patron, Jack Thornton.

Jack Thornton's mother tells Margaret of the threatened strike of the workers at her son's mill:

'There is some uncomfortable work going on in the town; a threatening of a strike.'

'A strike!' asked Margaret. 'What for! What are they going to strike for?'

'For the mastership and ownership of other people's property,' said Mrs Thornton, with a fierce snort. 'That is what they always strike for. If my son's work-people strike, I will only say they are a pack of ungrateful hounds. But I have no doubt they will.'

'They are wanting higher wages, I suppose?' asked Mr Hale.

'That is the face of the thing. But the truth is, they want to be masters, and make the masters into slaves on their own ground. They are always trying at it; they always have it in their minds; every five or six years, there comes a struggle between masters and men. They'll find themselves mistaken this time, I fancy, – a little out of their reckoning. If they turn out, they mayn't find it so easy to go in again. I believe the masters have a thing or two in their heads which will teach the men not to strike again in a hurry, if they try it this time.'

Not long afterwards, Margaret visits the home of a mill-worker with whose daughter she has made friends. His workmate is expressing fears about how the strike is affecting his family, especially his sick wife:

'It's no use, Higgins. Hoo* cannot live long a' this'n. Hoo's just sinking away – not for want o' meat hersel' – but because hoo cannot stand th' sight o' the little ones clemming*. Ay, clemming! Five shilling a week may do well enough for thee, wi' but two mouths to fill, and one on 'em a wench who can welly earn her own meat. But it's clemming to us. An' I tell thee plain – if hoo dies, as I'm 'feard hoo will afore we've getten th' five per cent, I'll fling th' money back i' th' masters' face, and say, "Be domned to yo'; be domned to th' whole cruel world o' yo'; that could na leave me th' best wife that ever bore childer to a man!" An' look thee, lad, I'll hate thee, and th' whole pack o' th' Union. Ay, an' chase yo' through heaven wi' my hatred, – I will, lad! I will – if yo're leading me astray i' this matter. Thou saidst, Nicholas, on Wednesday sennight* – and it's now Tuesday i' th' second week – that afore a fortnight we'd ha' the masters coming a-begging to us to take back our work, at our own wage – and time's nearly up, – and there's our lile Jack lying a'bed, too weak to cry, but just every now and then sobbing up his heart for want o' food, – our lile Jack, I tell thee, lad!'

*hoo she   *clemming starving   *sennight a week ('seven nights')

Teachers' note Give each pupil a copy of this page. Read the passages aloud to the class and help the pupils with any parts they do not understand. Ask them, working in groups, to re-read the first passage from the novel and to make notes about how they feel towards the Thorntons and towards the workers. They should then re-read the second passage and note any changes in their feelings. Talk about how the way in which the text is written affects their response to the situation. Discuss the effects of powerful verbs and adjectives and the expressive use of non-standard English.

Developing Literacy
Text Level
Year 8
© A & C BLACK

Past prose

- Choose a book by another nineteenth-century novelist. Record the ways in which the writer tells you about the social conditions of the time.

How does the writer show his or her views? How does the writer use language to engage the reader's feelings?

Title:	Author:

What the book tells you about the social conditions of the time

The writer's views about social conditions of the time	Evidence of the writer's views

Examples of language which engages the reader's feelings

NOW TRY THIS!

- Record the year in which the book was first published. Find out more about the social conditions at that time.

- Make notes about whether these social conditions are reflected in the book, and how this is done.

Make links between the book and your work in history.

!

Teachers' note The pupils could choose a book they have read or they could read extracts from a suitable novel. They could first make brief notes about the social conditions for different people at the time and their own opinions about these. Then ask the pupils to examine the writer's views and how they are expressed through the characters and events of the novel.

Put prose in its place
STARTER

- Read the passage. Look for clues about the place and culture in which the novel is set.

Sade is a Nigerian girl. A car has just screeched up to her home and a shot has been fired from the car, killing her mother.

'Is that the home of Mr Folarin Solaja who writes for *Speak?*'

The man's voice was soft but perfectly clear.

'Yes.'

'Don't trouble him. Just give him a message. Tell him: if we get the family first, what does it matter?'…

Papa, seated beside the desk in a full-length ink-black *agbada**, hardly seemed to notice as they settled themselves by the untidy side table stacked with books and papers.

It was usually their father whose arms, hands, even fingers, danced like furious gymnasts whenever he argued or talked about things that fired him up. It was usually their uncle who folded his arms as he listened. If you are a lawyer, Uncle Tunde had told Sade, you need to keep cool and listen very carefully. But today their father's arms hung without life. It was his older brother whose hands pleaded along with his voice.

'They're not finished with you, Folarin! They won't stop until they've shut you up. You know what that means! You've gone too far with them now.'

Their father always took chances with what he wrote. He said nothing now, but Sade knew his words.

The truth is the truth. How can I write what's untrue?

Sade knew how worried Mama had been about his latest article. But Sade had never heard Mama try to stop him, like Uncle Tunde did.

Their uncle stretched across the desk to pick up a newspaper. One hand resting on their father's shoulder, he began to read aloud: 'Why do the Brass Buttons who rule over us spend millions of naira* sending their children to the most expensive schools and colleges in England and America? How does a soldier – even a General – acquire so much money? And what about our own schools and colleges here in Nigeria? Our Brass Button Generals shut them down when teachers complain they have not been paid and when students complain they have no books. It seems they can still sleep easily in their beds even though hundreds of thousands of our own children are not being taught. What a disgrace for a country that held some of the finest universities and schools in Africa! But then our Commander-in-Chief believes more in buttons than brains.'

Normally Papa would have flared up.

Every word of that is true.

But today he was mute. His face was turned to the window that overlooked the front gate where the car had stopped. Their uncle slid the newspaper back on to the desk.

'You call your article "Our Children's Future". What do you imagine will happen now to your own, Folarin?'

***agbada** (language: Yoruba) A man's robe, usually embroidered

***naira** Nigerian currency

From *The Other Side of Truth* by Beverley Naidoo

Teachers' note Give each pupil or pair a copy of this page. Ask the pupils to read the passage in groups, then to discuss and make notes about anything they notice which reflects the culture and setting of the novel. Encourage them to look beyond material items and language; you could link this to the activity on pages 28–29 and remind them of the ways in which nineteenth-century social conditions in northern England were revealed in the passage from *North and South*. Ask what the pupils can deduce about the situation in the country in which this novel is set.

30

Developing Literacy
Text Level
Year 8
© A & C BLACK

Put prose in its place

- On the chart, record how the passage from *The Other Side of Truth* reflects the culture and place in which it is set.

Title and author:		
Setting and culture:		
Ways in which the novel reflects the setting and culture		
Names	**Language**	**Everyday items**

What seems to be going on in the country at the time, and how you can tell

NOW TRY THIS!

- Do some research about events in Nigeria in the 1990s. Make notes about your findings.
- Comment on what the writer of *The Other Side of Truth* is saying about them.

You could look up these people on the Internet: the writer Ken Saro Wiwa; the Ogoni People; General Abacha.

Teachers' note For the extension activity, the pupils will need access to the Internet or other resources. You could use the plenary session to discuss how culture and setting are reflected in other novels the pupils have read. For homework, the pupils could add notes on this topic to their personal reading logs.

Room for improvement
STARTER

- Cut out the paragraphs and sub-headings.
- Match the correct sub-heading to each paragraph.
- Write adjectives in the gaps to make the place sound more appealing.

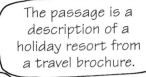

The passage is a description of a holiday resort from a travel brochure.

Wherever you stay, a _____ beach is generally within walking distance. Schools cater for all windsurfing abilities, and the diving off Los Lobos is said to be _____ .

These days there is a good selection of resort amenities, including many _____ restaurants and traditional tapas bars. There are still relatively few nightclubs but the resort has a fair number of _____ bars, some with music. The vast majority of these amenities, including a _____ selection of shops, are concentrated around the _____ town centre.

Within the bay are several _____ beaches, between which lie stretches of _____ volcanic coastline. Hearty souls may like to take a stroll along the coastal path that winds its way between the town and the dunes.

Originally a _____ fishing village, Corralejo has expanded over the last few years to become the _____ resort on the north of the island. The town centre, with its fishing harbour, ferry port serving Lanzarote and main commercial area, lies at the northern tip of a _____ bay. This bay sweeps south for some two or three kilometres before it meets the _____ expanse of sand dunes on the outskirts of the town.

Sub-headings

The surrounding area	**Amenities in the resort**
Beach facilities	**The town**

Teachers' note Ask the pupils to work in pairs and give each pair a copy of this page. Explain that there may be more than one way of ordering the paragraphs. The pupils can also use more than one word in each gap. They could experiment with changing adjectives to see the impact; challenge them to turn a positive impression into a negative one simply by changing a word. At the end of the session, discuss ways of ordering the paragraphs; point out that the paragraph introducing the town should come first.

Developing Literacy
Text Level
Year 8
© A & C BLACK

Room for improvement

• Use the proofreading symbols on the chart to correct the passage below.

Symbol	Meaning	Symbol	Meaning
⋏	**Insert something here** Example: It opend one eye then the other.	⌣	**Remove space** Example: It sat motion less on the path.
⊙	**Full stop** Example: He taunted the cat It scratched him.	/ or ⊢	**Delete something** Example: Cats are are nocturnal animals.
⸴	**Apostrophe or single quotation mark** Example: The cats tail twitched.	⌐⌙	**Transpose (swap round) letters or words** Example: He looked the in tree. Somethign looked back.
" "	**Double quotation marks** Example: Come here she commanded.	≡ under letter	**Change to capital letter** Example: His name was trevor.
Y	**Insert more space** Example: He gave it a biscuit.	⌐	**Start a new paragraph** Example: ...went to sleep. The next day...

Like childen, kittens love to play.They are pratcising and learning their hunting and killing skills Why not join in with your kittens games Wiggle a piece if string and and watch your pet pounce. make sure it is along piece of string though, or you those needle-sharp claw might cause you an indjury! There is a huge range of cat toys' on the market these days some costing small a fortune. I'm not spendig that much on my pet, you hears people say. Well, if you dont got twohundredpounds to spend, don't worry ! you is not an unwourthy owner at all Home -made toys do the job just as well – in fact the bestest toys ever are boxes!

NOW TRY THIS!

• Rewrite the following passage using the correct layout and punctuation.

• Ask a partner to read your passage and to correct any mistakes using the proofreading symbols.

• Discuss any mistakes and how you can avoid making them in future.

No room! No room! said the March Hare and the Mad Hatter to Alice there's plenty of room she replied indignantly and sat in a large arm-chair at one end of the table have some wine said the March Hare and he continued to drink his tea but I don't see any wine there's nothing but tea Alice responded the March Hare giggled that's because there isn't any the Hatter laughed too

---

Teachers' note The pupils could work in pairs. Explain that the passage can be corrected in different ways. Discuss that punctuation and spelling are only two factors in redrafting; paragraphs, the length of sentences and the audience and purpose are also important factors. During the plenary session, discuss the effects of different ways of punctuating and paragraphing the passage.

Cool comparisons
STARTER

- Read the passage. Say whether the underlined words and phrases are [similes] or [metaphors]. Discuss what they are comparing.
- Explain how the similes and metaphors help you to picture the setting in your mind.

A simile is a comparison which uses 'like' or 'as': for example, *she sang like an angel.*

A metaphor compares things by saying one is the other: for example, *the river was a ribbon of moonlight.*

How can a world be made of glass? What is the author really seeing?

How are things locked-up and sealed? What gives this impression?

It was <u>a world of glass</u>, sparkling and motionless. Vapours had frozen all over the trees and transformed them into <u>confections of sugar</u>. Everything was rigid, <u>locked-up and sealed</u>, and when we breathed the air it <u>smelt like needles</u> and <u>stabbed our nostrils</u> and made us sneeze.

Having sucked a few icicles, and kicked the water-butt – to hear its solid sound – and breathed through the frost on the window-pane, we ran up into the road. We hung around, waiting for something to happen. A dog trotted past <u>like a ghost in a cloud</u>, panting his aura around him. The distant fields in the low, weak sun were <u>crumpled like oyster shells</u>.

Presently some more boys came to join us, <u>wrapped like Russians</u>, with multi-coloured noses. We stood round in a group and just gasped at each other, waiting to get an idea. The thin ones were blue, with hunched up shoulders, hands deep in their pockets, shivering. The fat ones were rosy and <u>blowing like whales</u>; all of us had wet eyes. What should we do? We didn't know.

From *Cider with Rosie* by Laurie Lee

Why do the trees look like cakes or sweets? What picture does this create?

Do needles have a smell? How can the air 'stab'? What is the author imagining?

Teachers' note Photocopy this page onto an OHT. First revise similes and metaphors, then read the passage with the pupils and explain that this is a child's view of the world. Identify the similes and metaphors in the first paragraph and stress the importance of being able to describe their effect. Then split the class into groups and give each a paragraph to discuss. Build up vocabulary which will help the pupils to talk about the language effects: for example, *it gives me the impression of... it makes me think of... it creates a picture of...* They should always give reasons in support.

Developing Literacy
Text Level
Year 8
© A & C BLACK

Cool comparisons

• Read the poem. Then complete the chart to show how the poet uses personification .

Fog

Curling gently,
Almost cuddling, winding in and out,
The fog weaves itself softly around my legs.
It rubs its face along the rough walls
As it slides along the street,
Drifting,
Blurring the lighted windows with its thick pelt
As it purrs to be let in.
But now, rejected from the warmth,
It hisses around the orange glow of the lamps
Trying to destroy the light,
And sneaks off, merging into the horizon.

Personification means describing an object by giving it a person's or animal's characteristics.

Word	How it makes me think of a human or animal
curling	*It's like a cat curling around your legs to attract attention or show affection.*
cuddling	
rubs	
face	
pelt	
purrs	
hisses	
sneaks	

• Explain how personification helps you to imagine the fog.

_____

_____

NOW TRY THIS!

• Draw a chart like the one below. Use it to plan a poem about a windy day. Use personification to help readers imagine the wind and how it affects things, such as trees.

• Write your poem.

Subject of poem:	
Parts of the human/animal body I can use	**Human/animal actions I can use**

Teachers' note First revise personification and discuss how giving an object human or animal features can bring it to life and make it easier to imagine. Point out that personification is a form of metaphor: for example, the wind might have a voice and a body; trees could have moving arms and fingers.

Tone up!
STARTER

- Cut out the cards.
- Take turns to pick a card. Speaking in the way suggested on the card, say the sentence:

> I would like a drink.

- How many different ways can you say the sentence? Describe how the **tone** of your voice changes, and why.

informing	pleading
requesting	giving an order
threatening	shouting
begging	demanding
mumbling	complaining

Teachers' note Split the class into groups of four or five and give each group a copy of this page. First discuss that tone is the way in which something is said, and varies depending on the audience and purpose of the statement. Ask the pupils to cut out the cards and to experiment with tone of voice. Encourage them to discuss how the tones they use relate to the intended audience and purpose. At the end of the session, you could ask the pupils to consider how tone can be conveyed in writing.

Developing Literacy
Text Level
Year 8
© A & C BLACK

Tone up!

- Think of different ways of expressing each sentence so that it gives the same information in a different way. Describe the **tone** of each sentence you have written.

Example: *You won't be needing that.*

New sentences	Tone
I don't think you'll be needing that.	*informal, polite*
Believe me, you <u>won't</u> be needing that.	*informal, authoritative*
Something tells me you won't be needing that!	*informal, light-hearted*
That will not be required.	*formal, impersonal*

1 I would like to talk to you.

New sentences	Tone

2 Henry VIII was a headstrong man.

New sentences	Tone

3 Some people are afraid of spiders.

New sentences	Tone

NOW TRY THIS!

- Choose one of the sentences you have written. Use it as a starting point for a paragraph. Make the tone of your writing consistent throughout the paragraph.

You could write fiction or an information text. Convey the tone through your choice of words.

Teachers' note Point out that language helps to communicate tone, so the pupils will need to change the wording of each given sentence. Discuss useful words for describing the tone of a statement or request. The plenary session could involve a speaking and listening activity in which the pupils read out their sentences; discuss how different words are stressed as the tone changes.

Developing Literacy
Text Level
Year 8
© A & C BLACK **37**

Time for an update
STARTER

- Read this part of a poem about Little Red Riding Hood.
- Compare it with the original fairy tale. List the ways in which this version is different.

What does this retelling of the story aim to do?

'*What great big ears you have, Grandma.*'
'*All the better to hear you with,*' the Wolf replied.
'*What great big eyes you have, Grandma,*' said Little Red Riding Hood.
'*All the better to see you with,*' the Wolf replied.

He sat there watching her and smiled.
He thought, I'm going to eat this child.
Compared with her old Grandmamma
She's going to taste like caviare.

Then Little Red Riding Hood said, '*But Grandma,*
what a lovely great big furry coat you have on.'

'That's wrong!' cried Wolf. 'Have you forgot
'To tell me what BIG TEETH I've got?
'Ah, well, no matter what you say,
'I'm going to eat you anyway.'
The small girl smiles. One eyelid flickers.
She whips a pistol from her knickers.
She aims it at the creature's head
And *bang bang bang*, she shoots him dead.
A few weeks later, in the wood,
I came across Miss Riding Hood.
But what a change! No cloak of red,
No silly hood upon her head.
She said, 'Hello, and do please note
'My lovely furry WOLFSKIN COAT.'

From *Revolting Rhymes* by Roald Dahl

Teachers' note Split the class into groups of three and give each group a copy of this page. The pupils can dramatise the poem in groups, assuming the starts of the two characters and the narrator. Ask them to compare the poem with the original fairy tale and to list their ideas. Invite feedback; discuss who is the audience of this retelling and how the pupils can tell. You could go on to talk about how other traditional tales might be given a similar treatment.

Developing Literacy
Text Level
Year 8
© A & C BLACK

Time for an update

• Read the fable. Think about the moral of the story.

A fox fell into a well and could find no way out because the walls were too steep. At last a thirsty goat came to the well. The goat saw the fox and asked him if the water was good to drink. The fox replied that the water was wonderful, and encouraged the goat to come and join him. The goat thoughtlessly jumped in. The fox immediately jumped onto the goat's back and levered himself out using the creature's horns. Off he ran, leaving the goat stuck in the well.

• Plan a modern version of the fable. Use the same moral but change the characters and situation to bring it up to date.

Moral of the story: _____

Location	Characters
Situation at beginning of story	**Actions of characters**
Dialogue between characters	**Situation at end of story**

• Write your story.

NOW TRY THIS!

• Choose a traditional story or fairy tale. Write a version using the same theme and story structure, but set in modern times.

You could use these ideas:

☆ Snow White lives in a big city with seven short gangsters.

☆ Cinderella finds out that the prince is not the least bit charming.

☆ Goldilocks sneaks into someone's house and causes havoc with modern technology.

Teachers' note First discuss the conventions of fables and ensure that the pupils understand the idea of a 'moral'. Stress that the theme and moral should remain the same in the retelling, but that the characters, location and situation can change. Suggest that speech is used to make the story livelier and to make more of the characterisation.

All kinds of poems
STARTER

- Label each poem with its correct poetic form.
- Discuss what you notice about these poetic forms. Comment on the patterns, the line lengths and the use of rhyme.

Poetic forms

ballad	cinquain
couplet	free verse
haiku	sonnet

1

At evening when the lamp is lit,
Around the fire my parents sit;
They sit at home and talk and sing,
And do not play at anything.

Now, with my little gun, I crawl
All in the dark along the wall,
And follow round the forest track
Away behind the sofa back.

From 'The Land of Story-Books'
by Robert Louis Stevenson

2

There came three men from out of the west
Their victory to try;
And they have ta'en a solemn oath,
Poor Barleycorn should die.

They took a plough and ploughed him in,
Clods harrowed on his head;
And then they took a solemn oath
John Barleycorn was dead.

From 'John Barleycorn' (Traditional)

3

The gallows in place.
All watch with curious eyes
Then leave in silence.

Anon.

4

Composed upon Westminster Bridge, 1802

Earth has not anything to show more fair:
Dull would he be of soul who could pass by
A sight so touching in its majesty:
This City now doth, like a garment, wear
The beauty of the morning: silent, bare,
Ships, towers, domes, theatres, and temples lie
Open unto the fields, and to the sky:
All bright and glittering in the smokeless air.
Never did sun more beautifully steep
In his first splendour, valley, rock, or hill:
Ne'er saw I, never felt, a calm so deep!
The river glideth at his own sweet will:
Dear God! the very houses seem asleep:
And all that mighty heart is lying still!

William Wordsworth

5

September
Dry leaves –
Yellow and red –
Changing the world picture,
Make magic of the dying world.
Once more.

Traditional

6

Manhattan… Rich, hemm'd thick all round with sailships and steamships – an island sixteen miles long, solid-founded,
Numberless crowded streets – high growths of iron, slender, strong, light, splendidly uprising toward clear skies:
Tide swift and ample, well-loved by me…

From 'Leaves of Grass' by Walt Whitman

Teachers' note Photocopy this page onto an OHT. Read the poems with the pupils and invite them to identify the poetic forms. Discuss the distinctive features of each poetic form, focusing on the use of couplets, the rhyme scheme, the number of lines and the number of syllables in each line. You could talk about the advantages and disadvantages of writing in these forms. It may also be useful to consider whether certain poetic forms are more relevant to certain subject matter.

Developing Literacy
Text Level
Year 8
© A & C BLACK

All kinds of poems

• Read these poems, which both have death as their theme.

A Epitaph

Here lies a poor woman who was always tired,
She lived in a house where no help was hired.
The last words she said were, 'Dear friends,
    I am going
'Where washing ain't wanted, nor mending,
    nor sewing.
'Don't mourn for me now, don't mourn for me never;
'I'm going to do nothing for ever and ever.'

Anon.

B Death

Death is like an animal.
Don't think you can play –
Or daily bring your favourites, smiling and holding
    them out like a subservient friend.
It will not love you.
It will slowly take you over, just when you think you
    have mastered it, like a creature in the circus ring.
Many have tried to trap it behind the bars of their
    little tricky cages,
But it always escapes.
No sleep… no thought…
It acts on instinct
Travelling from house to house in the darkness.
Death is from everywhere – and yet from nowhere.
It is your enemy – but treat it like a friend.

Les Ray

• What do you think each poet's purpose was in writing the poem?

A: _____

_____

_____

B: _____

_____

_____

• Write about the poetic forms: the patterns you notice, the line lengths and the use of rhyme.

A: _____

_____

_____

B: _____

_____

_____

_____

• Write about the style of each poem. Is its **tone** serious or light-hearted? How does the choice of language convey the tone?

A: _____

_____

_____

_____

B: _____

_____

_____

_____

NOW TRY THIS!

• Write about how the form and style of each poem affect the way you respond to it.

Think about these questions:

☆ Do you like the way the poems are written? Why?

☆ Do you think either of the poems is too serious or too light-hearted? Why?

☆ What would each poem be like if it were written in a different form and style?

Teachers' note Ensure the pupils understand that 'theme' is not the same as 'content'. During the plenary session, discuss the difference in tone between the two poems. Identify the differences in form which reflect this, such as the jaunty rhythm and rhymes of the epitaph and the free verse of the serious poem which creates a solemn, even threatening, mood.

Guide the reader
STARTER

- Look at this information from a Design and Technology textbook. Explain how the author organises the material to guide the reader.

Wet or Dry?

Timber can expand and contract according to the weather. When a tree is cut down it contains quite a lot of water in its trunk and branches. If it is allowed to dry out under cover, it will **contract** (shrink) in width and become lighter in weight. It will not shrink very much in length. This drying-out process is called **seasoning**.

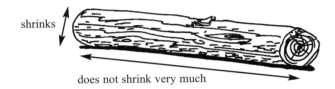

shrinks

does not shrink very much

Investigate wood

1. Take a dry, wide board and cut a strip of wood across the grain. Carefully measure the length of this strip. Soak the strip in water for 30 minutes, then measure the length again. Are the two measurements the same?
2. Now cut a length of chipboard or plywood and repeat this investigation. Do you get the same results? Why?

If timber swells or shrinks according to the weather, this must affect the way timber is used in Design and Technology. It is not surprising that most modern pieces of furniture are made from manufactured boards which do not swell or shrink when they are in use.

- Can you think of what may happen to a table top if it swells when it is firmly screwed to the table frame?
- Look at the floorboards at home. Can you see how the problem of shrinking and swelling is overcome?

Tongue and grooved floorboards

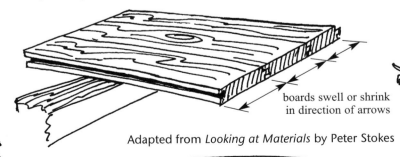

boards swell or shrink in direction of arrows

Adapted from *Looking at Materials* by Peter Stokes

Why is the title in a bold typeface?

Why are certain other words in bold type?

How does this diagram help?

Why is this section in a box? Why does it use a different typeface and numbered points?

Why are two different typefaces used here? Why are bullet points used?

What is the purpose of this diagram?

Teachers' note Photocopy this page onto an OHT. Read the passage with the pupils and discuss the organisational devices, using the questions as starting points. Draw out the use of different typefaces and sizes, the use of boxes, numbers and bullet points, and how diagrams are included at important times. All of these make the subject matter easier to understand. Discuss when it is appropriate to use such devices and point out that many things the pupils write should not make use of them.

Developing Literacy
Text Level
Year 8
© A & C BLACK

42

Guide the reader

- Read this passage about how laws are passed in England. The information is muddled and not all of it is relevant.

- Write the relevant parts in the correct order on the lines beneath.

There are five relevant sections of the passage. Start by underlining these and numbering them.

!

After this, a bill is presented to the House of Commons. It is debated in various stages. During this time, Members of Parliament can propose changes or amendments. These need to be voted upon by all MPs present. To make and then pass a law in England, the government first seeks advice from experts. These can be professionals, such as lawyers, or members of the public. Then, with the help of civil servants, it will prepare a law in draft form. A government has an executive (policy) role, a legislative (passing new laws) role and a judicial role. Finally, when both Houses approve the bill, it becomes law. Government business is carried out by a large group of officials called civil servants. This is not a new idea: ancient civilisations such as China had them many thousands of years ago. The government then creates a 'green paper' – a document which sets out its intentions. This is discussed and debated in Parliament. When this has happened, a revised 'white paper' is published. At the current time, when the new bill has been passed by the House of Commons it goes on to the House of Lords, although there are plans to change this. The Lords debate the bill and can block the bill's progress. They can return it to the Commons to be debated once again.

How laws are passed in England

_____

_____

_____

_____

_____

_____

_____

_____

_____

_____

_____

_____

_____

NOW TRY THIS!

- Use the information to produce a leaflet for parents to show what you are studying in Citizenship lessons. You could use ICT.

Consider how diagrams, numbers or bullet points could help to guide readers through the text.

Teachers' note First discuss the need for a logical order in, and progression between, events in the passage. The correct order of the relevant sections is given on page 8. During the plenary session, discuss the use of connectives (such as *after this*, *then*, *although*) and consider their function: for example, suggesting an alternative or indicating a time sequence.

Crystal clear
STARTER

- Read this scientific explanation. What is wrong with it?
- List ways in which it could be improved. Think about:

what you need to know at the start	the order of the explanation

the use of technical language	the use of language suitable for the subject

Pour about 1 pint of water into a saucepan. Add 100g of pretty white alum powder. Then you heat it all up. Don't forget to stir it or the powder will be all sticky! Then add loads of alum powder until no more disappears.

Let the mixture cool, then pour a bit into a saucer and stand it somewhere cool. Oh and I nearly forgot – pour the rest of the stuff into a glass jar.

After a few days, little twinkly crystals will start to grow in the saucer. Leave them until all the solution has evaporated, then choose the biggest as your seed.

Oops – you need to stir an extra tablespoon of alum into the glass jar to make a 'saturated solution'. Cover the jar with a clean cloth – not a grotty old one!

Now what you have to do is... (this is the fun part)... tie a long thread around your lovely seed crystal and wind the other end around a pencil. The crystal should grow for about two weeks. When it stops growing, take it out of the jar and wrap it in a piece of tissue. Hang the crystal in the solution by balancing the pencil across the jar. Put the jar somewhere nice and warm.

This is the way to grow crystals.

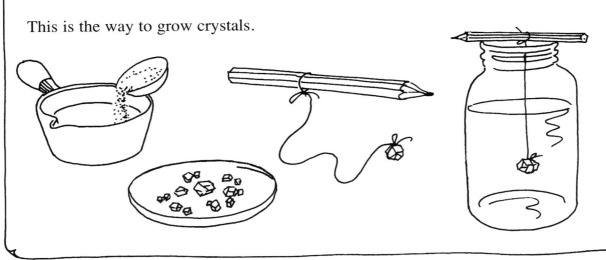

Teachers' note Split the class into groups and give each group a copy of this page. Read the passage together and discuss what is wrong with it, then ask the groups to discuss and list improvements. Invite feedback; ask what stylistic features the pupils expect from a scientific explanation, and why.

Developing Literacy
Text Level
Year 8
© A & C BLACK

Crystal clear

• Look at the diagram. It shows how the signal is sent when you make a call from a mobile phone.

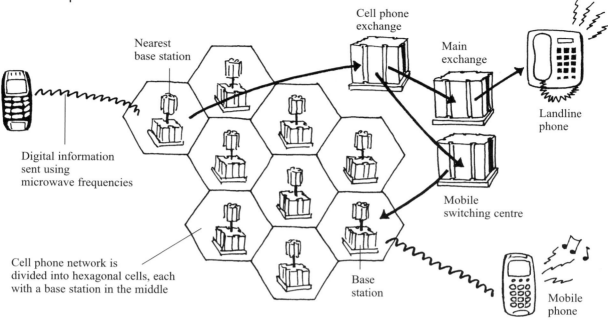

Cell phone exchange

Nearest base station

Main exchange

Landline phone

Digital information sent using microwave frequencies

Mobile switching centre

Cell phone network is divided into hexagonal cells, each with a base station in the middle

Base station

Mobile phone

• Use this chart to plan an explanation of the process, without using diagrams.

Title:	
Introduction	
Step 1	**Step 2**
Step 3 **or**	**Step 4** **or**
Conclude the process	

NOW TRY THIS!

• Write the explanation in full, without using diagrams.

Use **connectives** such as *first, then, if* and *finally. Use and explain the technical vocabulary.*

!

Teachers' note Remind the pupils that an explanation should use chronological order, the third person and connectives concerned with sequence, cause and effect and result.

Get formal!

STARTER

Use an appropriate degree of formality

Each card shows a different way of asking for a sandwich.

- Cut out the cards.
- Take turns to pick a card. Think about the situation in which the request might be used. Say what the speaker, audience and situation might be.
- Is the request formal or informal? What is the attitude of the speaker?

Fetch me a sandwich.	I say! A small sandwich at this time of day would be awfully appetising!
No words – just pointing.	Oi, mate, fetch us a sandwich, eh?
Bring me two slices of white bread containing flour and other permitted flavourings, surrounding another edible substance.	Could I have a sandwich please?
Sandwich!	I'd like a mouth-watering concoction of farmhouse loaf, lathered with creamy butter and encasing the most succulent oak-smoked salmon.
Would you mind terribly bringing me a sandwich please?	Isn't anyone selling sandwiches around here?

Teachers' note Split the class into groups and give each group a copy of this page. The pupils should go round the group, each taking a turn to pick a card and answer the questions. Remind them of the impact of audience and purpose on language and style. Discuss how the level of formality is indicated by vocabulary, sentence length and structure, and the use of standard or non-standard English. You could ask the pupils to imagine what the reaction might be if an informal request were made in a formal situation, and vice versa.

46

Developing Literacy
Text Level
Year 8
© A & C BLACK

Get formal!

- Read this version of a school prospectus. Discuss with a partner what is wrong with it.

Stonard County School is a really strange mixture of old and crumbling buildings. My mum says it's like a prison. The Lower School (in Kynaston Road) is where Years 7, 8 and 9 go; when you get to 14, you end up in the Upper School (if you stay that long), about a mile away in the old town. This is a pain to get to and boy does it waste endless amounts of time! It's also really expensive on the bus. Every September, six more forms of suckers join the school – 186 more rowdy pupils that other schools don't want. Everyone says there is specialist accommodation, but it ain't really true. They're mostly just normal classrooms – nine Science laboratories (ha, ha), four workshops, four wicked computer rooms, two gyms where we play footy, and two large playing fields where you can hide out when you skive off.

- Rewrite the school prospectus, using an appropriate level of formality.

> You will need to leave out some parts! Think about the audience and purpose.

- Continue the prospectus on another piece of paper. Give information about term dates, times of the school day, and form groups.

NOW TRY THIS!

- Write a prospectus for your own school, for new pupils in Year 7. Use these headings:

| Our aims and objectives | The Year 7 curriculum |

| School clubs and activities | Behaviour and discipline |

| School uniform |

> Remember to use the correct degree of formality.

Teachers' note Ensure the pupils realise that a school prospectus should be a piece of formal writing, and why. You could first identify what is wrong with this passage in the first few sentences and invite suggestions for a new version. During the plenary session, you could discuss the likely consequences if this version of the prospectus were published!

The art of persuasion
STARTER

- Read the passage.
- Discuss and list the arguments George Orwell uses against competitive sport.
- Underline examples of persuasive devices: for example, repetition, | rhetorical questions | and strongly emotional words.

Rhetorical questions are asked for effect. They do not require answers from the audience.

Nearly all sports practised nowadays are competitive. You play to win, and the game has little meaning unless you do your utmost to win. On the village green, where you pick up sides and no feeling of local patriotism is involved, it is possible to play simply for the fun and exercise: but as soon as the question of prestige arises, as soon as you feel some larger unit will be disgraced if you lose, are not the most savage combative instincts aroused? Anyone who has played in a school football match knows this. At the international level, sport is frankly mimic warfare. But the significant thing is not the behaviour of the players but the attitude of the spectators, of the nations who work themselves into furies over these absurd contests…

As soon as strong feelings of rivalry are aroused, the notion of playing the game according to the rules always vanishes. People want to see one side on top and the other side humiliated, and they forget that victory gained through cheating or through the intervention of the crowd is meaningless. Even when the spectators don't intervene physically, don't they try to influence the game by cheering their own side and 'rattling' opposing players with boos and insults? Serious sport has nothing to do with fair play. It is bound up with hatred, jealousy, boastfulness, disregard of all rules and sadistic pleasure in witnessing violence: in other words it is war minus the shooting.

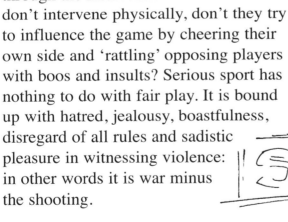

Adapted from *Shooting an Elephant and other essays* by George Orwell

---

Teachers' note Ask the pupils to work in pairs and give each pair a copy of this page. Allow them to read the passage aloud, as if it were a formal speech, in order to identify the persuasive devices used. Ask them to think about how effective the persuasion is and how Orwell achieves this. Towards the end of the session, invite feedback and discuss what the pupils think of Orwell's views on sport. Encourage them to suggest contrasting views with reasons and evidence (for use in the consolidation activity).

Developing Literacy
Text Level
Year 8
© A & C BLACK

The art of persuasion

- Write a reply to George Orwell in which you defend international sport. Answer his arguments and include points of your own. You could use the words and phrases in the bubbles.

> Think about how you will use **rhetorical questions** and other devices such as repetition. **!**

I understand your view that...

Furthermore...

Even if...

Just because... it does not follow that...

Surely...

Dear Mr Orwell,

However, I believe that... because...

I do not agree that... because...

Moreover...

Consider...

It is clear that...

NOW TRY THIS!

- Write text for a school poster encouraging pupils to get involved in competitive sports. Adapt your arguments above to the new audience and purpose.
- Make notes on how the audience and purpose influence the style of your writing.

Teachers' note Model with the pupils how they can develop ideas into arguments by using the words and phrases in the bubbles, in the order in which they appear. Stress that evidence must be included in order to create a persuasive argument. During the plenary session, discuss how pupils who completed the extension activity adapted the style and tone to the new audience and purpose.

Take my advice
STARTER

- Read these two different kinds of advice.
- List the characteristics of each type.

1

The Firework Code

★ Keep fireworks in a closed box.

★ Follow the instructions on each firework carefully. Read them by torchlight – NEVER a naked flame.

★ Light the end of the firework's fuse at arm's length.

★ Stand well back!

★ Never return to a firework once lit.

★ Never throw fireworks.

★ Keep pets indoors.

2

How to choose the right training shoe for the marathon

The first step in finding the right training shoe is to consider your running needs. These will include the type of surface (road, trail, track, and so on) you usually run on.

The second step is making sure you buy a shoe with the right shape for you. This relates to the length and width of your foot and to the height of your instep.

Performance training shoes

▶ Performance training shoes are lighter or more responsive versions of standard trainers.

▶ They're for fast-paced training or racing.

▶ You should buy these if you're a quick runner who wants a light shoe for fast-paced training; or if you'd like a racing shoe, but want more support and cushioning than you'd get from racers.

Look at the types of verbs used.

What is the **tone** of each text and how is it conveyed?

What is the purpose of the advice?

How does the author make the messages clear?

Look at how sub-headings and other features help to organise the texts.

Teachers' note Photocopy this page onto an OHT. Read the two passages with the class, then use the questions to help the pupils focus on the stylistic features. Draw out that these are examples of two different kinds of advice: direct guidance which uses the imperative (command) verb form, short sentences and bullet points for instructions; and the gentler kind which uses longer sentences, is more informative and offers suggestions less forcefully. List the characteristics of each type and discuss appropriate uses for each.

Developing Literacy
Text Level
Year 8
© A & C BLACK

Take my advice

Six teenagers were asked: 'How good are you at saving money?' Read their answers.

> Terrible! If I earn any money I go straight out and spend it on music or DVDs.

> I spend tons on texting my mates. I can't live without my mobile phone!

> I know what I have to spend each day on bus fares and school dinners, so I try to work out a budget and stick to it.

> I'm hopeless! I spend all my pocket money on magazines, snacks, jewellery, CDs…

> I'm trying to save up for some new football boots but it's really hard – I just don't know where my pocket money goes.

> I put money into my savings account regularly but I have to keep raiding it for birthday presents and stuff.

- Write an advice leaflet for people in your class about how to manage their money. Give ideas for saving and keeping track of money, how to budget for the week, and where to get further advice.

NOW TRY THIS!

- Write text for a poster to advise young people about National Insurance payments and income tax when they leave school. Use the information below.

You will be sent your personal National Insurance number and card while you are in Year 11. You will be asked for the number when you start a new job or training placement. Your employers will then deduct a contribution from your wages and these contributions go towards benefits and pensions in the future.

Income tax is deducted from your wages together with National Insurance on a regular basis, either weekly or monthly depending on how often you get paid. Your employer usually works out how much tax you have to pay and then takes it out of your wages to pay the Inland Revenue. Income tax is used to pay for things like defence, policing, health, education and social security.

Teachers' note Suggest that the pupils brainstorm and list their own ideas for advice on managing money. They could research personal finance on the Internet or using other sources. Remind them of the importance of using an appropriate tone and suitable language for the kind of advice being given.

Analyse this
STARTER

- Think about whether mobile phones should be banned from public places. Note down a few points for and against.

For banning mobile phones in public places

Against banning mobile phones in public places

- Cut out the cards. The words are all alternatives to the verb 'to say'.
- Take turns to pick a card. Use the word in a sentence for or against banning mobile phones in public places.
- Say how the word creates a different impression from the verb 'to say'.

You can make up things people might have said about the issue.

allege	argue	assert
believe	claim	comment
complain	contend	declare
maintain	observe	predict
state	stress	suggest

Teachers' note Split the class into groups and give each group a copy of this page. Allow two minutes for the pupils to brainstorm arguments for and against the issue. Then model how to use the verbs in sentences: for example, *Many people complain about annoying ringtones; Kim Taylor stressed that dangers from radiation should not be ignored.* Encourage the pupils to avoid expressing personal opinions in the first person. They can change the tense of the verbs: for example, *predicted, stressed.* Revise reported speech and the use of *that* to introduce subordinate clauses.

Developing Literacy
Text Level
Year 8
© A & C BLACK

Analyse this

- Read the information about waste and the environment.
- Use the chart to help you plan a balanced analysis of whether recycling is worthwhile.

Think of other points you could make as well.

!

Every year in the UK, each person throws away half a tonne of drinks cans, bottles, magazines, food packaging and other waste. There are three simple steps we can all take to help prevent waste: Reduce – Re-use – Recycle. Landfill (in which sites or tips are filled up with alternate layers of rubbish and earth) can pollute surface water and groundwater when the rubbish decomposes. Scientists have shown that the decay of rubbish can also generate gases including methane, a greenhouse gas which damages the ozone layer. The problem can be helped by reducing the waste we generate and recycling all we can.

Financially it makes sense to minimise our waste; the cost of waste collection and disposal continues to rise.

Recycling helps to conserve our dwindling stocks of natural resources. Environmental campaigners say that recycling glass and paper saves on fuel and produces less gas to destroy the ozone layer.

Some people think that the recycling process creates more waste (for instance, harmful greenhouse gases) and so it is better just to use landfill. It costs more to recycle paper than to make it from trees.

Points for recycling	Points against recycling

NOW TRY THIS!

- Write your analysis. Present both sides of the argument and be objective. Use the phrases on the notepad to help.

Some people claim that… because…

However, others assert that…

It has been suggested that…

They argue that…

The evidence for this is…

On the other hand…

Teachers' note Tell the pupils that some ideas for the analysis are given in the passage but that they should try to think of and research more. For the extension activity, it will be useful to revise the use of paragraphs and the need for an introduction and conclusion. Remind the pupils to make use of the language and sentence constructions from the starter activity.

Developing Literacy
Text Level
Year 8
© A & C BLACK **53**

Telling tales
STARTER

• This diagram can help you to tell a story. First think about these questions.

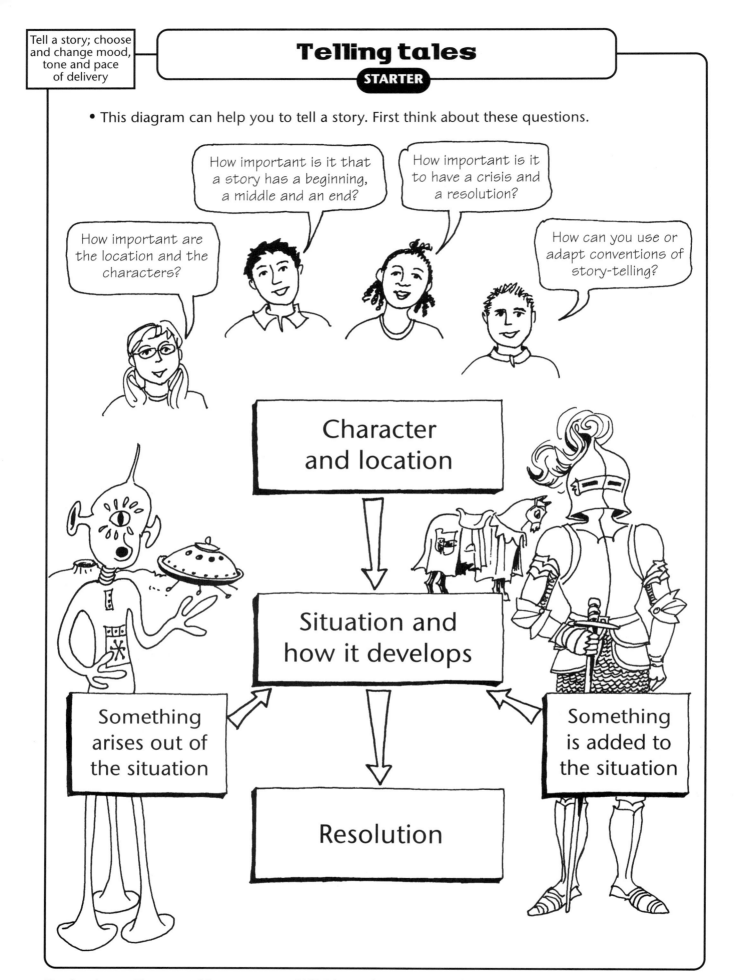

How important are the location and the characters?

How important is it that a story has a beginning, a middle and an end?

How important is it to have a crisis and a resolution?

How can you use or adapt conventions of story-telling?

Character and location

Situation and how it develops

Something arises out of the situation

Something is added to the situation

Resolution

Teachers' note Photocopy this page onto an OHT. Discuss the questions in the bubbles with the class, with reference to traditional tales or short stories the pupils have read. Talk about how well the stories follow the structure outlined on the flow chart. Emphasise that although a story needs a beginning, a middle and an end, it does not have to be told in chronological order; techniques such as flashbacks can be used to add suspense. Ask the pupils to discuss possible story-telling techniques in groups. The flow chart should then be used with the consolidation activity.

Developing Literacy
Text Level
Year 8
© A & C BLACK

Telling tales

- Cut out the cards. Choose a ⬚ genre ⬚ and use the two cards to help you determine the characters and setting of your story.

- Choose any one of the situation cards.

- Tell a story using your three picture cards. Follow the conventions of the genre. You could use the situation to add a twist to the usual type of plot.

Genre: Science fiction
Characters:

Genre: Crime and detectives
Character:

Genre: Fantasy
Character:

Genre: Science fiction
Setting:

Genre: Crime and detectives
Setting:

Genre: Fantasy
Setting:

Situation:

Situation:

Situation:

NOW TRY THIS!

- Now cut out these cards. Choose one to add to your story. How does it change the story's **mood**, **tone** or **pace**?

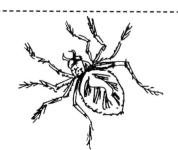

Teachers' note Display the starter OHT so that the pupils can refer to the flow chart. Ask them to work in pairs; one pupil should begin and develop a story for five minutes, then carry out the extension activity and complete the story within another five minutes. Then it is the turn of the second pupil. During the plenary session, discuss how the way a story is told adds to its effect.

Speak formally
STARTER

- Read the passages. In the first one, Shazia and Connor are chatting to a small group of new pupils as they show them around the school. The second passage is from a formal welcome talk they give to all the new pupils.

- Make notes about the differences in language between the two passages.

1

Hi! I'm Shazia. This is Connor. We'll show you where everything is in a mo, but we have to do the uniform first. This is it, just like we've got – grey. There's a special tie for each year. Ours are green for Year 8. Year 7 have blue. You can't wear jeans and you need trainers and tracksuits for PE. You have to wear black shoes – sensible ones. What d'you think that means? Yep – no ninety-metre-high platforms or heels like needles and all that. The teachers let you write the rules yourselves, but then you've got to keep them. Yeah – really! They… the teachers know we're not stupid. Some jewellery is OK – you can have little ear studs and even bracelets as long as they're not massive. It's… er… it's for safety and that sort of stuff. Don't even think about tongue studs or body-piercing! OK?

OK Shaz, I'll do my bit now. Over there – see the lockers? They're for all yer gear. But we don't nick stuff 'ere. It just makes ya feel better if stuff's locked up, doesn't it? You get yer first key free but if you lose it you've gorra pay a pound for another. You geddit back when you leave. That's about it, but it's all in the book you get. Um… right, I'll tell you about lunch. You can have school dinner. You gerra choice and pay wi' yer swipe card. It's the same if you're on free ones. You get the same swipe card as if you pay, so no one knows the diff'rence. Or bring yer own stuff and there's a nice room – look – in there, wi' the red tables. There's the water machine. You don't have to use a grotty drinking fountain or yucky metal jugs. Oh, there's a water machine in the classrooms, too. We… you can gerra drink when you want as long as you don't mess about. You get treated like a grown-up 'ere as long as you act like one and don't mess.

So… d'you want to ask us anythin' or is that enough? You can come an' ask anytime you're stuck or get lost or anythin'. You can ask anyone. They're all OK 'ere.

2

Hello and welcome to Middale School. My name is Shazia and this is Connor. We are going to give you an introduction to all the things you need to know to get started: uniform, PE clothes, storing your belongings, meals and so on. Then you'll be given a guided tour to find out where everything is. We know how easy it is to get lost in a large building, so some of us will be wearing 'Welcome new pupils' badges. It is our job to help you, but you can ask anyone.

We'll begin with the uniform. The main colour is grey: grey trousers for boys and grey skirts or trousers for girls, but each year group has its own tie and sweatshirt colour. Katie is wearing the Year 7 colours, Rosie has Year 8 and Hassan has Year 9. Shoes should be black and the only rule is that they are 'sensible'. Later you can tell us what you think that means. Your ideas will be listed and put in a file for the teachers. Then the teachers expect you to keep to the rules you have made. Some jewellery is allowed: small ear studs, watches, even bracelets, but absolutely no body- or tongue-piercing. This is for safety reasons.

Next I will show you the PE kit, and then Connor will take over and tell you about lunchtime.

Teachers' note Split the class into small groups and give each group a copy of this page. Ask the pupils to highlight the words and phrases which show differences in the level of formality of the passages. Invite feedback; identify the differences between formal and informal language (see page 9). Discuss why a more formal type of language is used in the second passage. You could ask the pupils how they would change it for a handbook for the parents of new pupils or for a leaflet to give to school inspectors.

Developing Literacy
Text Level
Year 8
© A & C BLACK

Speak formally

- Work with a partner. Tell your partner about a place you have visited and found interesting. Record one another's descriptions using a cassette recorder.

- Play back the recording and transcribe it.

Speak informally – don't plan what you are going to say. Speak for about two minutes.

Continue on another sheet of paper if you need to.

- How will you need to change your speech to make it into a formal presentation to the whole class or school? Underline the parts you will need to change. Look for:

- Non-standard English (for example, slang and non-standard grammar)
- 'Fillers' and hesitations (for example, *er*, *um*)
- 'Tag' questions (for example, *didn't they?*)
- Informal vocabulary (for example, *sort of*, *thingy*)
- Contractions (for example, *they've*)
- Repetition

- Note examples of the changes on the charts.

Non-standard English		Informal vocabulary	
Examples:	Change to:	Examples:	Change to:

NOW TRY THIS!

- Think about other changes you need to make, such as changing the order of the information or adding background details to help your audience's understanding.

- Write your presentation.

Teachers' note Encourage the pupils to chat informally. Each pupil should take a turn at speaking and then transcribe his or her spoken words. Encourage them to transcribe everything, including 'fillers' such as *er* and *um*. During the plenary session, discuss examples of the changes the pupils made to their speeches. Give them the opportunity to make their presentations in another lesson.

From pictures to words

STARTER

- Take turns to explain to a partner how to do the stretching exercise in the picture.
- Make notes about any problems you have in following the instructions your partner gives you.

> Does your partner give enough detail? Is the information in the correct order? **!**

Notes on _____**'s instructions**

Notes on _____**'s instructions**

Example:

Hamstring – muscle at back of thigh

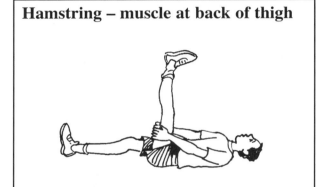

> Lie on your back. Bring your left knee towards your chest and place your hands around the lower thigh. Then straighten your leg so that your heel points to the ceiling. With your hands behind your thigh, gently pull your raised leg a little further towards your chest. Make sure you keep your back flat on the floor.

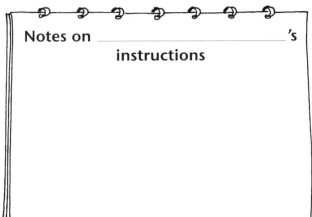

Quadriceps – muscle at front of thigh

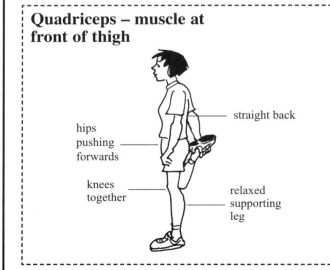

hips pushing forwards

knees together

straight back

relaxed supporting leg

Calf muscle

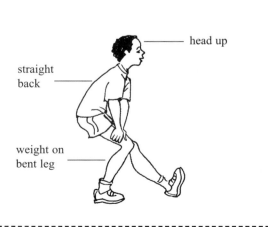

head up

straight back

weight on bent leg

Teachers' note Ask the pupils to work in pairs. Make a photocopy of this page for each pair and cut off the two pictures at the bottom. Give a picture to each pupil in the pair and ask them not to show each other their pictures. Emphasise that this is a speaking and listening, and not a writing, activity; each pupil needs to communicate a message as clearly as possible to a partner. The listener should listen carefully, then attempt to perform the action described. Encourage the pupils to evaluate the structure and content of each other's explanations.

Developing Literacy
Text Level
Year 8
© A & C BLACK

From pictures to words

- Cut out the cards.
- Imagine you are the director of a film and the pictures are shots from your storyboard. Arrange them in a meaningful order.
- Explain to a partner how the pictures tell a story.
- Try telling the same story using the pictures in a different order. How many versions can you make?

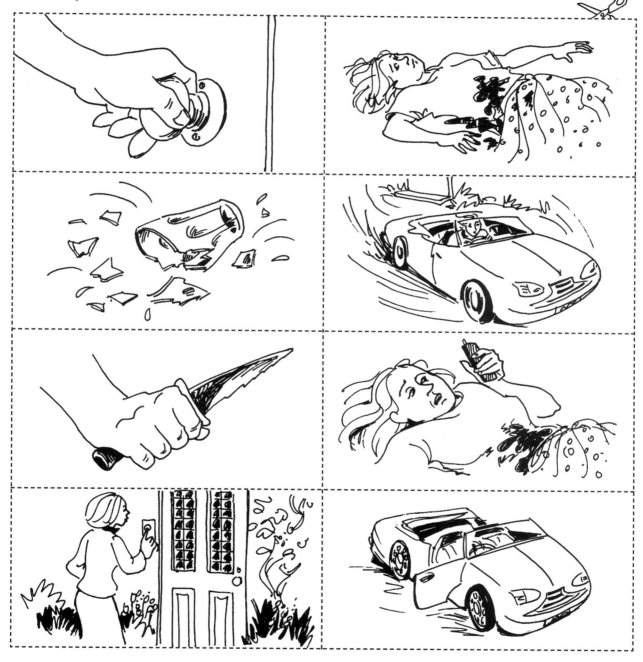

NOW TRY THIS!

- Make notes for a | commentary | to go with your story.

Describe the significance of each shot.
Explain the relationships between the shots.

!

Teachers' note Stress that the pictures can be interpreted and sequenced in a variety of ways. The pupils may write notes for their story but should not write it out in full. During the plenary session, discuss the effects of structuring the story in different ways. The scene could be dramatised in another lesson using music or other sound effects.

It's the way you say it

- Cut out the role cards and share them out between the people in your group.

- Focus on one of the statements and requests. Go round the group, with each of you making the statement or request in role.

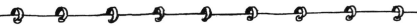

Statements and requests

1. Ask the person to look at something.

2. Ask the person if you can have a look at something.

3. Ask for help with something.

4. Tell the person that there is no point in making a fuss about something.

5. Ask the person if he or she knows where something is.

6. Tell the person that you think he or she has made a mistake.

Make up suitable details for the statement or request.

Role cards

①	②	③
The managing director of a company speaking to a student on work experience	A student on work experience speaking to the managing director	Someone of your own age speaking to a friend
④	⑤	⑥
A parent speaking to a very young child	A shop manager speaking to a police officer	Someone of your own age speaking to a person in charge of a public place (such as a library)

Teachers' note Split the class into groups of up to six and give each group a copy of this page. Invite one group of pupils to make one of the statements or questions in role. The rest of the class should listen and then comment on the differences in tone, choice of words and emphasis. Continue, with each group having a turn. Discuss why the pupils alter their way of speaking and even the words used when speaking to different people in different situations. Draw out that changes in tone and choice of words do not necessarily involve changes in politeness.

Developing Literacy
Text Level
Year 8
© A & C BLACK

It's the way you say it

- With a partner, choose one of the statements or requests. Make notes on the chart about the different ways in which it was expressed by people in different roles.

Statement/request: _____

Role number	Exact words spoken	Tone of voice	Stressed words/words on which the speaker's voice rose
1			
2			
3			
4			
5			
6			

You could use underlining and punctuation to help.

- Write a short dialogue between several people who would address one another in different ways. Find ways of showing how each person speaks as well as what he or she says.

NOW TRY THIS!

Teachers' note The pupils will need to refer to the starter activity resources. For further practice, you could play tape recordings of people speaking (perhaps from radio or television) and ask the pupils whom each speaker might be addressing, and how they can tell.

Developing Literacy
Text Level
Year 8
© A & C BLACK

61

Adopt a role
STARTER

- Read this passage from *Watership Down*. Identify the roles taken by each rabbit in the discussion.

Think about who is making suggestions, developing ideas or trying to get everyone to agree.

The rabbits have left their warren because Fiver has sensed something terrifying there, although he doesn't know what the danger is.

Hazel moved close to Fiver and quietly edged him away from the others, feeding as he went. When they were a little way off, and half-concealed by a patch of reeds, he said,

'Are you sure we've got to cross the river, Fiver? What about going along the bank one way or the other?'

'No, we need to cross the river, Hazel, so that we can get into those fields – and on beyond them too. I know what we ought to be looking for – a high, lonely place with dry soil, where rabbits can see and hear all round and men hardly ever come. Wouldn't that be worth a journey?'

'Yes, of course it would. But is there such a place?'

'Not near a river – I needn't tell you that. But if you cross a river you start going up again, don't you? We ought to be on the top – on the top and in the open.'

'But, Fiver, I think they may refuse to go much further. And then again, you say all this and yet you say you're too tired to swim?'

'I can rest, Hazel, but Pipkin's in a pretty bad way. I think he's injured. We may have to stay here half the day.'

'Well, let's go and talk to the others. They may not mind staying. It's crossing they're not going to fancy, unless something frightens them into it.'

As soon as they had made their way back, Bigwig came across to them from the bushes at the edge of the path.

'I was wondering where you'd got to,' he said to Hazel. 'Are you ready to move on?'

'No, I'm not,' answered Hazel firmly. 'I think we ought to stay here until *ni-Frith**. That'll give everyone a chance to rest and then we can swim across to those fields.'

Bigwig was about to reply, but Blackberry spoke first.

'Bigwig,' he said, 'why don't you swim over now, and then go out into the field and have a look round? The wood may not stretch very far one way or the other. You could see from there; and then we might know which would be the best way to go.'

*ni-Frith noon

From *Watership Down* by Richard Adams

Teachers' note Photocopy this page onto an OHT. Read the passage with the class, then invite the pupils to share their ideas and to explain how they can recognise the role taken by each character in the discussion. Note that some characters take a more prominent role than others. Point out that in most discussions, different people take on different roles and this can be useful in achieving what is needed.

Developing Literacy
Text Level
Year 8
© A & C BLACK

Adopt a role

- In your group, discuss how to solve a problem. Two members of the group should act as observers, making notes of the discussion. The others should each take one of the following roles.

> Making suggestions

> Finding a consensus of opinion

> Developing ideas

> Gathering together the main strands of thought

- The observers should record the discussion here.

The problem

Ideas for solving the problem

Idea	Advantages	Disadvantages

The idea we think will work best, and why

How we can put the idea into practice

<table>
<tr><td>NOW TRY THIS!</td><td>• Write a report about the discussion. Use the notes taken by the observers to help you.</td></tr>
</table>

> Think about how well people fulfilled the roles and how the discussion could have been improved.

Teachers' note The pupils should work in groups of six; each group will need two copies of this page. Set a problem to discuss: for example, how to persuade other pupils to keep the school tidy or how to prevent bullying. Point out that, as well as discussing the problem, they need to be aware of *how* they discuss it. To achieve this, they should focus on their own particular role.

Glossary

accent The way in which words are pronounced, including: how 'open' or 'closed' vowel sounds are; the level of hardness of consonants; the emphasis or dropping of initial and final consonants; and the stress on syllables.

active (of a verb) A verb whose subject does the action: for example, *they shouted.*

adjective A word that describes a noun: for example, *blue, round, tall.*

adverb A word that gives information about a verb: for example, *she shouted loudly.*

agreement The match between words or phrases in terms of number, gender, case and person: for example, a singular noun requires a singular verb (*she goes, he walks*).

alliteration The repetition of a letter or sound at the beginning of words: for example, *lizards lounging lazily.*

chronological writing Writing organised so that events follow a time sequence.

commentary An explanation which gives further information about a text. This can be in note form.

connective A word or phrase used to link words, phrases, clauses, sentences or paragraphs: for example, *I like swimming but Jane prefers running; we go there whenever we can.*

connotation The emotional associations with a word or phrase.

contraction A shortened form of a word in which an apostrophe replaces omitted letters: for example, *you're (you are).*

dialect A form of slang used in a particular place. It includes non-standard English words such as *gan* for 'go' (northeast England) and *bairn* for 'child' (Scotland and northeast England).

edit To modify written work to produce a good version for publication.

ellipsis (plural *ellipses*) Three dots (...) which show that words in a passage have been missed out. Ellipses are also used to show that spoken words or a train of thought are trailing off.

fact A statement which can be checked and verified in more than one source.

fiction An invented version of events – the creation of the writer.

genre A term used to describe different kinds of writing, each characterised by particular features: for example, science fiction, mystery.

imperative The command form of a verb: for example, *go, mix, take.*

irony This is when something does not match what is expected and is presented in a way that mocks a situation.

jargon A form of language which includes technical terms and is used by members of a group: for example, politicians, sailors or chess-players.

key words The important words in a passage, which indicate its topic.

metaphor A comparison which says one thing *is* the other: for example, *the river is a ribbon of moonlight.*

mood (of a text) The emotional 'feel' of a text (for example, it could make the reader feel exhilarated, joyful, excited or sad).

non-chronological writing Writing that does not follow the restrictions of a time sequence: for example, a report organised according to characteristics.

non-standard English Spoken or written language which includes the use of unconventional grammar. It may contain slang and dialect expressions.

noun A word that names a person, place or thing: for example, *a river, the Thames, a tributary.*

onomatopoeia The use of words which echo sounds associated with their meanings: for example, *boom, squeak.*

passive (of a verb) A verb whose subject has the action done to it: for example, *the ball was kicked by the girl; the money was stolen.*

person (of a verb) This can be singular or plural: for example, *I go, we go* (first person); *you go* (second person); *she goes, they go* (third person).

personification A way of describing an object by giving it human or animal characteristics.

rhetorical question A question asked for persuasive effect, which does not require an answer from the audience.

scan To look at a text quickly, to locate key words and ideas.

simile A comparison which uses *like* or *as*: for example, *she sang like an angel.*

skim To read a passage to gain an overview of the subject matter.

slang A form of non-standard English which is used by a particular group of people: for example, according to where they live or their interests.

standard English Spoken or written language which uses the conventional rules of grammar.

syllable A rhythmic sound unit of a word. Each syllable should contain at least one vowel or a *y*: for example, *al/though* has two syllables; *syl/lab/le* has three.

tense The form of a verb that indicates time (past, present or future).

tone The way in which something is expressed: for example, ironically or casually. In writing, language and punctuation help to convey tone.

verb A word or group of words that indicates action or a state of being: for example, *is, grew.*

Developing Literacy: Text Level Year 8 © A & C BLACK